The Ballad of Aucassin and Nicolette

A Play in Three Acts

THE BALLAD OF AUCASSIN AND NICOLETTE

A Play in Three Acts

BY CHARLES CAUSLEY

WITH MUSIC BY STEPHEN MCNEFF
AND ILLUSTRATIONS BY YVONNE GILBERT

KESTREL BOOKS

KESTREL BOOKS
Published by Penguin Books Ltd,
Harmondsworth, Middlesex, England

First published in 1981

ISBN 0 7226 5698 X

Printed in Great Britain
by W & J Mackay Limited, Chatham

To Ian Watson

CONTENTS

INTRODUCTION

by Richard Williams, the director of the first production

Aucassin and Nicolette is a versatile text which can be staged as a large-scale pageant or, as in the original production, an intimate piece of story-telling with a few actors. We used a company of six, which is the minimum. Apart from the two acting Aucassin and Nicolette, the actors were obviously involved in considerable doubling and trebling.

At the end of the play we had to sacrifice the re-entry of the Viscountess because of the small company. Her lines were spoken by our second actress, but as a member of the Court, not as the Viscountess. With a larger company it is possible to offer many such 'cameo' rôles – Oxboy, the Watchman as well as the Viscountess – to individual actors and actresses.

Each director should arrange any doubling according to the talents and size of the company – allowing each actor time to change his costume and gather his props! In our production the company sat at the side of the acting area on cushions watching the action when not playing a part, but obviously this depends on the numbers involved. Changes of costume mainly took place in view of the audience, and I think this succeeded in giving the effect of informal story-telling.

Our set was based on a medieval pageant tent, with two paralleled curtain rails, each with three curtains. With the front curtains open and the back closed an enclosed 'interior' space was created. With all the curtains hanging separately the forest could be suggested, and by the actors holding up white curtains sails of the ships could be suggested. Whatever set is used, simplicity should be the keynote.

The story is charmingly straightforward, with characters whose passions and interests are similarly single-minded, and the design of the play should not complicate it. Our costumes were based on medieval shapes and outlines, but because a full costume treatment would have been prohibitively expensive we used modern materials – often from surprising sources. A car scrap-yard supplied some armour, many of the weapons, and the decorations on the costumes! For the moat into which Nicolette falls on her escape from prison we used an army camouflage net, under which the actors variously stood and knelt. Again nothing is laid down so we tried to find various and (hopefully) ingenious solutions to the production problems. Martin Oxboy was played by our smallest actor, who simply brought on a chair with false feet fixed to it to stand on, and whose costume then fell to the floor over the chair.

The Ballad Singer is an important element in the play, but the part does not have to be restricted to a single actor. We used whoever was available, apart from Aucassin and Nicolette. It is important to remember that many of the scenes are witty and comic – indeed the original was a satirical look at Courtly Love – so the tone of the performance should be bright and clear. Whatever approach you decide to take, you should keep the action clear, simple and fast-moving.

Above all, enjoy telling the story.

The first performance of *The Ballad of Aucassin and Nicolette*, commissioned with funds made available by South West Arts, was presented by South West Music Theatre as part of the Exeter Festival on 27 May 1978, with the following cast. The first London performance was at the King's Head Theatre Club on 3 July 1978. In the London production, parts taken by Tim Iremonger were played by Charlie Peacock.

Robert Karas	AUCASSIN
Paula Bent	NICOLETTE
Tim Iremonger	GARIN, COUNT OF BEAUCAIRE; TOM; MARTIN OXBOY; KING OF CARTHAGE; MARINER
Janet Howd	COUNTESS OF BEAUCAIRE; OLD WOMAN; QUEEN OF TORELORE; VISCOUNTESS
Alan Gill	BOUGARS, COUNT OF VALENCE; WATCHMAN; JOHNNY; KNIGHT; TARIK, A SARACEN CAPTAIN
Philip Fox	VISCOUNT; DICK; KING OF TORELORE; PALMER

Directed by Richard Williams

The first broadcast performance of the play was given by the BBC on Radio 4, on 12 May 1980, with the following cast:

Ian Caddy	BALLAD SINGER
David Firth	AUCASSIN
Imelda Staunton	NICOLETTE
David Gwynne	BOUGARS, COUNT OF VALENCE
Peter Woodthorpe	GARIN, COUNT OF BEAUCAIRE; TARIK, A SARACEN CAPTAIN
Janet Howd	COUNTESS OF BEAUCAIRE; OLD WOMAN (singer)
Philip Fox	VISCOUNT; DICK; KING OF CARTHAGE
June Marlow	OLD WOMAN; QUEEN OF TORELORE
John Bull	WATCHMAN; KING OF TORELORE
Adrian Egan	JOHNNY; MARTIN OXBOY
David Timson	TOM; KNIGHT

Additional chorus: Stephen Foulkes, Clare Griffel, George Hubbock, Jennifer Jillich, Mollie Petrie, Cyril Royall, Margaret Small, Hubert Tucker.

Oxford Pro Musica Orchestra, conducted by Stephen McNeff

Directed by Brian Miller

THE BALLAD
OF
AUCASSIN AND
NICOLETTE

14

CHARACTERS

Aucassin, *son and heir to the Count of Beaucaire*
Nicolette, *a Saracen*
Garin, Count of Beaucaire
Countess of Beaucaire
Viscount
Viscountess
Bougars, Count of Valence
Old Woman
Watchman
Johnny ⎫
Tom ⎬ *shepherds*
Dick ⎭
Knight
Martin Oxboy, *a ploughman*
King of Torelore
Queen of Torelore
Tarik, *a Saracen Captain*
King of Carthage
Mariner
Palmer
Baron
Ballad Singer
Lords, Mariners, Pirates, Sailors,
People of Torelore

The action of the play takes place during the thirteenth century in and about the city of Beaucaire, in a topsy-turvy Kingdom of Torelore, and at the court of the King of Carthage.

The first two acts should be virtually a continuous presentation, with only a brief pause between them during which the house-lights should not be raised.

AUTHOR'S NOTE

The original story of Aucassin and Nicolette, told in a series of prose passages linked by lyrical poems, was first set down in the dialect of Picardy by an anonymous author early in the thirteenth century. Some scholars have suggested that as a purely spoken and sung piece it was in existence much earlier, and may have been Arabic or even Greek in origin. The written text, certainly, has always suggested to me that in its original form it was a piece performed by a minstrel, or a small group of travelling players.

When, in 1978, I was invited by South West Music Theatre to provide a play for the company, the musical settings to be by Stephen McNeff, I seized the opportunity of working on something I had long wanted to write: a version of this old French tale in the form of a three-act play with music. *The Ballad of Aucassin and Nicolette* is the result.

In this present form, the text will be seen to consist of a series of poems and ballads, linked by passages of prose dialogue, and with an absolute minimum of stage directions. This I have done quite deliberately, in the hope that any future stage presentations will be (as was the original production) as free and as creatively imaginative an interpretation of the piece as possible.

CHARLES CAUSLEY

ACT ONE

SCENE 1

[AUCASSIN; NICOLETTE; COUNT GARIN; COUNTESS; VIS-
COUNT; VISCOUNTESS; *revealed one by one. They stand in
emblematic attitudes resembling illustrations in a medieval
manuscript. Highly stylized movements as they mime the for-
bidden love of* AUCASSIN *and* NICOLETTE *by their two families
while the following is sung.*]

BALLAD SINGER: Listen, friend and stranger, well
    To the story that I tell,
How two lovers first were met –
    Aucassin and Nicolette;
And what noble deeds were done
    Till his own true-love was won.
Fair she was of form and face,
    And the mirror of his grace.
There is none who hears it sung,
    Be he old, he will be young;
Be he sick, he will be hale,
    Ripe of cheek that once was pale;
Be he sad, and he will smile
    If he hearkens for a while –
[*spoken*]   So fine the tale.

SCENE 2

[COUNT GARIN OF BEAUCAIRE *is being armed for battle by an
invisible attendant.*]

GARIN: God's teeth! To think that I –
Count Garin of Beaucaire –

Living on an overdraft of days
And a pension of breath
Should be leaned on so by such a lout as Count
    Bougars of Valence;
His brains slower than treacle,
His wits as thick as a cathedral door.
Had I but a son and heir to succeed me!
He should now wear this grating shirt of mail,
Drag on these steel fingers,
Waddle in iron leggings.

This great pot-helm upon my head
So stifles my identity
That even I begin to forget who I am
Till my squire here crowns me
With a reminder of coloured feathers;
Pins this painted triangle upon my arm
That I may name myself to myself
As well as to my enemies.

The name spelt on this longsword
In rubies, pearls, emeralds, should be my son's;
He should unseat my foe from his galloper
With this ash-lance, longer than a man –
Then excavate his skull with its shaft;
But the lot falls to me.

O for a child to lift these burdens!
But I have neither daughter nor son.
    [*He does not utter the name 'Aucassin', but mouths it.*]
All that heaven has dispensed to me
Is Aucassin. My boy Aucassin! Utter his name
I cannot. It falters against my gums;
Sinks like a stone down my throat's well.
Of Aucassin another must tell.

SCENE 3

[COUNTESS OF BEAUCAIRE *and* COUNT GARIN *sing. Pantomime during song: first encounter between* AUCASSIN *and* NICOLETTE; *they fall in love; dance.*]

COUNTESS: Aucassin is fine and fair,
           Salt-blue eye and yellow hair;

           Easy hand, and quick of heart,
           Blessed in every beating part;

           Light of limb, and sapling-strong –
           All good graces there belong:

           But Aucassin is a slave
           Of the mighty Prince of Love;

           Conquered is from foot to crown,
           Utterly is now cast down;

           Caught within a silken knot,
           All his duties now forgot:

           Sighs his days will not be spent
           Tilting at the tournament;

           Vows he never will be knight,
           Nor lug weapons to the fight;

           Swears he cannot, if he could,
           All his name and nature should.

GARIN: At my gate my foes are met.
           Jesu! Hear him!

AUCASSIN: [*a love-sick cry*]   Nicolette!

SCENE 4

[COUNT GARIN; COUNTESS OF BEAUCAIRE; AUCASSIN *gazing at a lily, and giving it an occasional sniff. Noise of siege and battle below.* GARIN's *opening words coincide with explosions.*]

GARIN: Auc-
               [*He tries again.*]
           -assin.
               [*Pause. Silence. Explosion.*]

AUCASSIN: I greet you, father.

GARIN: Go to! Take arms. Mount up! Away!
             Grasp your lands tight.
             Give heart to our men.
             If they spy you among them, armed and caparisoned,
             They will fight with the more fury
             For their bodies and belongings.
             Such as they are.

AUCASSIN: Such as they are not.
             If I have not Nicolette,
             I have nothing.

GARIN: [*explodes*]   Castle! A province of acres!
             Squads of liegemen!
             A cellarful of fortune!
             My good name!

AUCASSIN: I have nothing.
             Father, swallow your breath.
             I pray that God may never more
             Answer prayer of mine
             If I bear arms, ride to battle,
             Clout knight, blow for blow,
             Dissect foot-soldier,
             Unless you give me Nicolette,
             My sweet friend,
             Whom I love well.

GARIN: Put the maiden from your mind,
             Your ears are enchanted, your eyes are blind;
             A princess of princesses
             You shall find!

AUCASSIN: Never!

GARIN: Speak to him, wife.

COUNTESS: Nicolette is a slave girl, bought
             Of the heathen Saracen, and brought
             Here as captive by my Lord's liegeman,
             Viscount and Captain of this town –
             Who stood at the holy font, was godfather
             At her christening and raised her
             In his own house as his daughter.

GARIN: You long to leap with some maid
                Between the sheets? That's cause for comfort.
                I'll not name the manner of man I feared
                You might have been. If a wife's what you need
                Then I shall give you the child
                Of a King or a Count.
                Name me the richest man in all France!
                If it's his daughter you want
                You shall have her.

AUCASSIN: There is no throne in the world,
                Be it that of the Empress of Byzantium
                Or of Allemaigne,
                The Sovereign Queen of France
                Or of the Saxon English,
                To which my Nicolette would not bring an even
                Greater store of nobility and beauty,
                So filled is she with all graces.
                I shall marry none other,
                Nor fight in any battle neither
                Until such a day.
                Though my father rant and rail,
                Though my scolding mother wail.

COUNTESS: O a foolish boy is he,
                Weds a maid of low degree;
                Better he lay in his grave
                Than with one sold as a slave.
                Yet he cries . . .
                [*Mocking*]   'My only care
                Is for Nicolette the fair.'

AUCASSIN: For her beauty is as bright
                As a starfall through the night
                On Heaven's stair.

SCENE 5

[COUNT GARIN; VISCOUNT.]

GARIN: Sir Viscount, are you not my vassal, town captain, satellite, sizar, pensioner, dependant and creature?

VISCOUNT: God be thanked, my Lord.

GARIN: Answer me truly, then. If I wished your god-daughter Nicolette to wed my son, what would you say to that?

VISCOUNT: Alleluia!

GARIN: But if I desired you to send her away that they met no more, since – because of her – my son is no longer a son to me?

VISCOUNT: Amen. A. . .men!

GARIN: You speak from the heart?

VISCOUNT: Where else?

GARIN: Understand me, old friend. I love the child Nicolette. But if I could as much as lay a finger on her, I'd have her burnt at the stake. And no mistake.

VISCOUNT: [*mirthless; zombie*]   Ha! Ha!

GARIN: My love for her, and you, is broad and deep as the Middle Sea.

VISCOUNT: [*greyly; echoing*]   The Middle Sea.

GARIN: The Great Sea! [*Thumps him on the back.*] But get her out of my son's life, and out of mine, or it'll go badly with the pair of you.

VISCOUNT: Sire, this affair has no blessing from me, I can tell you. Lord Aucassin as a husband for my god-child? The thought never occurred to me. I intended her for a far humbler fellow. A mere starling; neither a glowing peacock nor a shining eagle.

              This is Aucassin's doing, none of mine, I can assure you. Since you disapprove of the match so strongly, she shall be sent to a country where their eyes may never meet again.

GARIN: See to it, good fellow. My affection and loyalty for you are stronger than mountains. But watch your step, my man.

              [VISCOUNT *smiles feebly and backs away; trips as he goes.* GARIN, *po-faced, regal stance, watches. Then moves off with great dignity; also trips.*]

SCENE 6

[*Music. Birdsong.* VISCOUNT; OLD WOMAN.]

VISCOUNT: Hear me now, old woman. You have been long enough in my service to know that only my Lord the Count in this land wields more power than I?

OLD WOMAN: [*pious gabble*]   Also the Good Lord who reigns on high and is for ever blessed, and whom I pray –

VISCOUNT: [*briskly*]   Also the Good Lord who reigns on high and is for ever etcetera, naturally.

OLD WOMAN: I doubt even the palace of heaven to be richer than yours, Sir Viscount. Or its gardens fairer than these.

VISCOUNT: And I have every intention that things shall so remain. Despite the fact that my beloved adopted daughter Nicolette the Saracen has committed the unpardonable error of falling in love with a young man quite beyond her in social station. And whose father proposes to match him with a Princess, or the daughter of an Emperor. It's extremely inconsiderate of my child. Thoughts of her, moreover, are distracting the young fellow from his filial duty.

OLD WOMAN: Filial duty – ah!

VISCOUNT: The defence of the realm.

OLD WOMAN: [*disappointed*]   Oh.

VISCOUNT: And that young man is son of Count Garin of Beaucaire. Young Aucassin.
[OLD WOMAN *gasps with horror.*]
I should be greatly obliged if you would desist from the farce of pretending that you know nothing of this.

OLD WOMAN: Put yourself in my place, my Lord. Wouldn't you?

VISCOUNT: Very likely. All the same, the affair is common gossip. You lie.

OLD WOMAN: Jane Know-all was hanged on Tuesday. But Jane Know-nothing lives to tell the tale. I wish to wear my head no farther from my shoulders than it now is.

VISCOUNT: Attend, then, that it may stay so. High in the garden tower that stands before us, Nicolette must be confined. You are to bear her company, and to guard that she does not escape. Bread and meat, water and wine, furniture and fresh linen shall be provided in plenty for you both. The door shall be sealed that none may come out nor enter in. And none – least of all her lover, my Lord Aucassin – is to know of Nicolette's presence there.

OLD WOMAN: But the couple are young, and eager. And love is strong.

VISCOUNT: Then your strength of purpose must make wall thicker, door stouter, tower taller. The pair must never meet again. If they do so, Count Garin has vowed to burn Nicolette in the fire, and Aucassin may well be the fuel. So – keep the door close, as you will your lips of this affair. Or summer will turn to a black winter for all of us.

OLD WOMAN: It is hard that life should be endured with a scarcity of light, and of God's air.

VISCOUNT: Let this gold I now give you illuminate your darkness. As for fresh air – throw abroad the window there that looks downwards on the garden.

OLD WOMAN To be a gaoler is also to be a prisoner, my Lord. What kind of life is that?

VISCOUNT: Small indeed. In fact, a kind of death. But, at least, a death with breath. Be thankful for that. And see to it that Nicolette is hidden from the sight of all people. That way, my Lord the Count may forgive. And Aucassin forget.

SCENE 7

[BALLAD SINGER *with pipe and drum. During song, dance-drama;* VISCOUNT *commands* NICOLETTE *to be confined in a tower with* OLD WOMAN *as company. Food, drink, furniture, etc. carried up. The tower door is sealed.*]

BALLAD SINGER: Tell you a story
    Old as Zion –
Pretty little lambkin
    Loved a lion.

Lion and lambkin –
   Man and wife?
Old man lion said,
   'Not on your life!

*'High-born blood
   Don't mix with low;
She ain't upsettin'
   My *status quo*.'

Found her a cage
   Till her ways she'd mend;
Shut her away
   From her loving friend.

Painted the walls
   With fields and trees;
Little black lamb
   Didn't fancy these.

Round the cage
   A garden grew
Where roses blossomed
   And wild birds flew.

They sealed the door
   With an iron pin –
No way out
   And no way in.

Food for hunger,
   Drink for thirst,
But love was what
   She wanted most.

For company
   An old, old ewe
In case the lamb
   Herself she slew.

Now I've heard it says
   In the Book of Worth
That Heaven won't come
   Upon the earth,

---

* This verse omitted in first production

And you won't lose sight
   Of the flames of Hell
Till lamb and lion
   Together dwell.

O you won't see a shine
   Of Heavenly weather
Till lion and lamb
   Lie down together;

And priest and prince
   And people agree
Of the Golden Age
   It's the golden key:

That lion and lamb
   Together lie down –
As long as it ain't
   In this here town.
   This here town,
   This here town.
As long as it ain't
   In this here town.

SCENE 8
[NICOLETTE *in her tower cell.* OLD WOMAN *spinning.*]

NICOLETTE: Would that I could fly as free
   As the bird upon the tree.
   In a painted cage of clay
   I am locked for love away.

OLD WOMAN: Turn the wheel and foot the tread;
   Spin me strong a lovers' thread.
   Turn the wheel and foot the tread;
   Spin a heart to rule a head.

NICOLETTE: Yet as strong as is the sea
   Do I know my love loves me.
   Son of Mary, hear me say –
   From this cell I must away
   With least delay.
     [*The wheel stops spinning and the* OLD WOMAN *falls asleep.* NICOLETTE *turns and regards her.*]

SCENE 9

[AUCASSIN; VISCOUNT.]

AUCASSIN: Has she gone to England,
        Has she gone to Spain,
    Has she gone to Muscovy,
        Will she come again?

    Is she sped with wine and bread,
        Or is it with a knife?
    Has she journeyed fifteen leagues
        Or fifteen years of life?

    Cure love here or kill it there:
        If I die of pain,
    You with your ten fingers
        Both of us have slain.

VISCOUNT: To the daughter of a Count,
    Child of a King –
        Give your body's silver,
        Gold of your ring.

    Had you taken Nicolette
    Naked to your breast –
        Then the furnaces of Hell
        Been your soul's unrest.

    All the days of all time
    There to sear and seethe –
        The fond airs of Paradise
        Never would you breathe.

AUCASSIN: Paradise? What is Paradise to me without my Nicolette? And think, my friend, of the company a soul keeps there for eternity.
    [*Sings, very fast patter-song.*]

    The uncomplaining beggar-man self-sanctified with
        sores,
    And cherubim and seraphim for ever forming fours;

    The singing, smelly friar humming by a holy font,
    The shivering and shoe-less who have lived a life of
        want;

The spotty and the dotty and the serious and sad,
And those so full of fearful joy they drive the good to
     bad;

The cold ecclesiastic barking dogma from a script,
And those who can't be happy unless coughing in a
     crypt;

The creepy chapel-crawler whose con-cep-ti-on of fun
Is listening to sermons, and who can't remember one;

The tiresome and the diresome and those bare of back
     and side,
And those who never had a taste for sin, and never
     tried;

Those who say that they anticipate with joy the Day of
     Doom
And think there's something missing here on this side
     of the tomb –

If this is Heavenly company
          For such I'll never fret,
          But burn with Nicolette,
          Burn with Nicolette.

VISCOUNT: [*speaks*]   My Lord, you have been drinking;
           It's the devil's thoughts you're thinking.

AUCASSIN: [*sings*]   If through the gates of Paradise step such of
               little ease –
           I choose not an eternity of such good folk as these.

           O if I lie in my love's arms I care not if I dwell
           Beside a lake of brimstone or upon the shores of Hell;

           For there go the fine churchmen in their silk and satin
                gowns,
           A-carrying their crooked sticks and wearing gilded
                crowns;

           And there go all the gallant knights a-killed in war or
                sport,
           And all the pretty nymphs who act no better than they
                ought;

And there the gentle ladies are, by prince and page
    ador'd,
With lovers two and lovers three – besides their loving
    lord;

O there the jolly archer points his arrow at the mark,
And even scores a bull's-eye when he's firing in the
    dark;

There go ermine and go sables and go gear of goodly
    worth –
And the poets and the players and the Kings of all the
    earth.

If these are those who go to Hell,
To Hell I shall repair –
If Nicolette is there,
Nicolette is there.

If these are Hell's companions,
Then they have no compare –
If Nicolette be there,
Nicolette be there.

VISCOUNT: [*speaks*]   Aucassin, you cry in vain
Nicolette to win again:
      She is near, and yet is she
      Dweller in a far country.
And that kingdom and its key
Does your father hold in fee –
      Never more that you may lie
      Limb to limb and eye to eye,
Never more your love to be –
Touch nor taste nor hear nor see:
      Or we wall must burnéd be
      By the wood of a green tree.

Aucassin, I bid you fair:
Of your father's love, beware –
Yet if your own death you'd cure,
All false love abjure. Abjure.

SCENE 10

[BALLAD SINGER; AUCASSIN.]

BALLAD SINGER: Aucassin in heavy dole
                  Homeward wandered, sad of soul;
                  None with words could heal his heart
                  Nor kind counsel could impart –
                  And as to a prison bare
                  Climbed he up his chamber-stair,
                  Where – unseen by friend or foe –
                  His stiff tears began to flow.

AUCASSIN: Nicolette – my only dear –
                  Be she far or be she near
                  Is of maidens all, the peer;
                  Be she living, be she dead,
                  Is of every maiden, head:
                  Fair in stillness, fair caressing,
                  Fair in kindness and in kissing,
                  Fair in duty, fair in leisure,
                  Fair in prayer and holy pleasure;
                  Yet within a bitter cell
                  For her love my love must dwell;
                  And as with a dagger's blade
                  In a grave my heart is laid,
                  Such is my woe.

SCENE 11

[GARIN; AUCASSIN; BALLAD SINGER; BOUGARS. *Assault on the castle by infantry and cavalry below. Alarms. Tuckets. Explosions.*]

GARIN: Wretched and cowardly boy! How can you see your best and strongest castle in such peril and do nothing to save it? Lose Beaucaire and you're a naked man. Never a stitch on your spine.
                  [*Trumpet.* GARIN *at window. Explosion.*]
                  Holy Blood! But Bougars of Valence is anxious to finish the war by supper-time by the look of things. It's a

devilish fate when a civilized man finds himself pitted against a greedy jobbernowl who observes nothing more clearly than the clock in his belly.

See how his horsemen and infantry beat their skulls and arms to jam on the castle gate! And how our brave fellows rush to defend the walls and hold them back!

[AUCASSIN *is totally uninterested.*]

My God! Even the townsfolk assist them by climbing the parapets and flinging down quarrels and sharpened stakes. My son! You cannot lie there, hoisting neither toe nor finger, and lose all your inheritance!

[*Explosion*]

But humbly I crave your pardon: I see that you can.

Sweet boy! Son! I implore you. Help your men. Arm yourself. Lightly. But lightly! A dagger. A pen-knife. No need to fight, or to be fought. The mere sight of you – poised on a bulwark or at an embrasure, swimming in the flood of war – will encourage our men to defend their holdings and havings. Yours and mine.

Come! A hardy, strong lad such as you may do this simple thing easily. [*Uncertainly*] Easily. Anyhow, it is your duty.

AUCASSIN: Do not ask such a thing of me, father. I have already vowed that this shall never be unless you give me Nicolette.

GARIN: Then it shall never be. Rather than see her wife or woman to you, I would lose all.

[GARIN *is leaving, slowly.*]

All.

[*Moves even more slowly, obviously hoping* AUCASSIN *will change his mind.*]

AUCASSIN: [*rises*]   Father, I will make a bargain with you.

GARIN: [*speeds back*]   A bargain? What manner of bargain?

AUCASSIN: I will take up my weapons and join myself in the heat of battle. If God brings me out sure and complete, whole as an egg, grant me permission to have two or three words with Nicolette.

GARIN: Agree . . .

AUCASSIN: And one kiss.

GARIN: [*dubious*]   . . . d.

> [AUCASSIN *is armed, and mounts hobby-horse.*]

BALLAD SINGER: Aucassin is filled with bliss
                       At the promise of a kiss
                  (Hundred thousand coin of gold
                       Cannot make him half so bold)
                  As he arms him for the press
                       Head to toe in iron dress.
                  Double-lined his shirt of steel,
                       Plume on helmet, spur on heel;
                  On a belt of leather made
                       Hangs his jewel-hilted blade.
                  Lance and shield in fingers bright
                       – Image of a perfect knight –
                  Calls his dearest love to mind,
                       And, more swiftly than the wind,
                  Pricks his springing charger fast
                       To the battle-front at last
                            – Towards the fight.

> [AUCASSIN *gallops about, but horse and rider remain stock-still, in heroic pose, at the following.*]

BOUGARS: [*voice off*]   Aucassin, son of Beaucaire, wake!
                  Your dreams of love dispel!
                  Count Bougars of Valence is come
                       To blow you all to Hell!

> [*Bellows with laughter.* GARIN *rushes out. A tremendous crash. Conflict. Uproar.* BOUGARS' *laughter suddenly changes to a great cry of fury.*]

CURTAIN

ACT TWO

SCENE 1

[BALLAD SINGER; AUCASSIN.]

BALLAD SINGER: His shield upon his shoulder,
      His helm upon his head,
He blazed into the battle
      With neither fear nor dread!

He neither thought of plunder,
      Nor pillage or of prize,
Nor how to place the thumping mace
      Between a foeman's eyes.

He beat no blade about him
      Nor struck a brutal blow
To cut or gash or slice or slash
      And lay a Christian low.

Of nothing was he minded
      As with the foe he met –
Except the form, except the face
      Of sweetest Nicolette.

The reins fell from his fingers,
      His sword hung still as stone,
As deep among his foemen
      His charger bore him on.

Fast as the barbéd arrow
      Leaps forward from the string –
Until his foemen lap him
      Within an iron ring.

They seize his rein! His shield they gain!
> They spoil him of his lance!
His hangmen cry, 'Now heaven high
> We'll make Aucassin dance!'

And never a word, it seemed, he heard
> Upon their bloody breath
Until they sought his life to thwart –
> Spoke of his death.

AUCASSIN: *His death?*

SCENE 2

[AUCASSIN, *ringed by enemies poised in extremely threatening attitudes.*]

AUCASSIN: Where am I? Hear me, Blessed Saviour! Now, who are these fellows?

> [*He examines them closely.*]

My God, but to a man they are my mortal enemies. With ropes and blades. What are they up to? I've a notion that if they don't lug my head from my body with a length of hemp, they'll nick it off with a long-sword. And if this little tree-top bids farewell to this little trunk, I shall never be able to bend to Nicolette again, and that's a fact. Well, my lad, you've still got a good cutter at your side, muscle in your arm, spunk in your loins, and your horse isn't winded yet. If I don't fight fierce as a zoo-ful of lions to keep my vital parts together for Nicolette's dear sake – and my own – may the Almighty never aid me more!

> [*He draws his sword and lays about him. The following is performed in the manner of an old-fashioned concert-party ensemble number; an elimination song-and-dance pattern. All sing; lines distributed as appropriate.*]

One for St Michael,
> One for his feast;
One for St George,
> And one for his beast.

One for the Magdalene,
    One for her jar;
Three for the Wise Men,
    One for the star.

One for St Stephen,
    One for his stone;
One for St Blaize,
    And one for his comb.

One for St Clement,
    And one for his hook;
One for St Paul,
    And one for his book.

One for Great James,
    And one for his shell;
One for St Clether,
    And one for his well.

One for St Dunstan,
    One for his tongs;
One for the Psalmist,
    And one for his songs.

One for St Mark,
    And one for his cat;
One, St Jerome
    And his Cardinal's hat.

One for St Crispin,
    The shoe and the leather;
One for St Swithin,
    And one for good weather.

One for St David,
    One for his dove;
One for the Virgin,
    And one for love.

One for St Benedict,
    One for his cup . . .
    [AUCASSIN *looks about. They are all vanquished. He strikes*
    an attitude.]

AUCASSIN: One for the singer . . .

    [COUNT BOUGARS, *armed, appears and steals quietly up behind him.* AUCASSIN *affects not to notice, then suddenly whirls round and gives* BOUGARS *a great Chaplin-esque thwack on the top of the helmet with the flat of his sword-blade. The head-piece splits in two, and we see* BOUGARS' *face as he reels and collapses.*]

    And one for luck.

    [AUCASSIN *seizes him by the nose and leads him off, still staggering.*]

SCENE 3

[GARIN *at the castle of Beaucaire.* AUCASSIN *leads in* BOUGARS, *who is on his knees, by the nose, and holds him so during most of the following encounter.*]

AUCASSIN: Father, I give you your chiefest enemy. One who has warred against you these twenty years; a tedious and bloody business, if you ask me, and something no man seems able to end.

GARIN: Better, then, that a young man should do his duty than indulge in day-dreams.

AUCASSIN: No sermons, father, please. Merely keep your promise.

GARIN: [*affecting to rack his brains*]   Promise?

AUCASSIN: If it's dropped out of a hole in your noble memory, it hasn't mine. The promise you made that if God brought me out of the fight unscathed as a baby in a good birth, you would permit me two or three words with Nicolette. And one kiss. Hold to your bargain, venerable father. Trade with me honestly.

GARIN: [*aside*]   God ha' mercy that necessity forces me into the role of a bad exemplar; and to my own son, too. If Nicolette is dead, or hid, or dwells in a far country, I know not. The which I shall never ask. Therefore, how may she meet Aucassin? [*Addresses him*] My mind is fixed. If Nicolette were here, she should be –

GARIN AND
AUCASSIN: Burnt at the stake.

AUCASSIN: Is that your last word on the subject?

GARIN: As God hears me.

AUCASSIN: And hear me. A black and deceitful tongue is a bad match for the white of your hair.

GARIN: Disobey me further and prison shall be yours.

AUCASSIN: Count Bougars of Valence, you are my captive.

BOUGARS: [*still on his knees and held by the nose*]   So it would seem.

AUCASSIN: [*releases his grasp and raises* BOUGARS *to his feet*]   Place your hand in mine.
    [BOUGARS *does so.*]
Swear that as long as you may live and as long as you are able, you shall never let day end without doing damage to my father, to his properties and possessions.

GARIN: Treachery!

BOUGARS: [*to* AUCASSIN]   Sir, I am your sorry prisoner. This is no time for jokes. Merely tell me what ransom I must pay for my life and freedom. Whether it is in gold or silver, horses for warriors or saddle-horses for ladies, skins or furs, hawks or hounds. You shall have it.

GARIN: Naturally.

AUCASSIN: I require none of these things, good fellow.

GARIN: My poor boy is bewitched.

BOUGARS: My Lord, are you sick?

AUCASSIN: In wit and health, never better. Allow me to remind you of the Articles of War. You are my prisoner. Grant me not my just request, then – should I so desire – I may strike your head from your body.

GARIN: [*staggered*]   Should he so desire? Why should he not so desire?

BOUGARS: Then I promise in the name of God to do what you ask of me.

[*Ritual. The vow is made.*]

AUCASSIN: Come, I will ride with you to neutral ground, and you
shall be set free.

[AUCASSIN *and* BOUGARS *go.*]

GARIN: Merciful God, tell me that my ears fib and that my eyes
tell a pedlar's tale. Clearly, my son's brains are fried to a
frizzle by the flames of love. So. I must place him behind
walls. For his own safety, of course. And, naturally, of
only the best marble. [*Calls*] Gaoler! Seek me, sure and
sound, prison deep in prison ground. [*As he goes*]

Stone walls, they say, make not a gaol,
Nor lock and bolt a cell;
But for a fellow without bail,
I vow they serve as well.

[*Calls*]   Gaoler!

SCENE 4

[PALMER. *As he sings, he produces two glove-puppets: one
recognizably of* NICOLETTE, *the other a replica of himself. He
manipulates the puppets to illustrate the action in the song.*]

PALMER: There was an old palmer of Limousin
Of Limousin was he;
He twisted and turned
And he babbled and burned
As though he had fevers three, my boys,
As though he had fevers three.

This palmer, they said, who lies here a-bed
Is plagued by demons galore;
And it won't be long
Till he hears the song
That they sing at the Heavenly door, my boys,
That they sing at the Heavenly door:
And never O never O never no more
Will this perishing palmer go pilgrimming more
For the good of his so-so-soul, my boys,
For the good of his so-so-soul.

Now just as this palmer of Limousin
Was dying there in the dirt,
Young Nicolette
Came walking by
And she lifted her ermine skirt, my boys,
And lifted her ermine skirt.
She bore up her train from the mud and the rain,
And she lifted her shift as well,
And the palmer caught sight
Of a limb so bright
That a miracle then befell, my boys,
A miracle then befell.

The palmer arose as his blood it unfroze
And his sickness it vanished like snow,
And for ever and aye for ten years and a day
A pilgrimming he did go, my boys,
A pilgrimming go-go-go.
And he swore that for him the sight of the limb
Of a lily-white lady fair
Was better by half than a doctor's draught,
And medicine free as air
Far better than a doctor's care,
And good for both body and soul, my boys,
For body and so-so-soul.
And good for both body and soul, my boys,
For body and so-so-soul.

SCENE 5

[NICOLETTE. OLD WOMAN, *asleep. Restless,* NICOLETTE *rises from her bed and escapes by knotting sheets, etc. and descending from window.*]

BALLAD SINGER: Sealed in a tower for love lay a lady
    – Cloudless the sky, and the month it was May –
As from its pillar of leaves the fond nightingale
    Over and over repeated this lay:

    'If those who hate you should hear of your hiding,
        Long in this world then you never will stay;

Lady, now hasten; come down from your prison –
      Seek you your lover with never delay.

'Spin you a rope; close it fast to your casement;
      Kilt up your kirtle and bare your bright feet;
Lightly now pass through the dew of the grass –
      Unbutton the postern, and tread the dark street.

'Find you that prison-house,' so sang the nightingale,
'Where in the moonglow your love lies alone;
Through the torn wall hear his voice as he calls to you,
      Part with your fingers its curtain of stone
            – That two lovers joy may win,
                  Though one lies out and one within.'

SCENE 6

[NICOLETTE *arrives by the dungeon where* AUCASSIN *is imprisoned, and hears his voice.*]

AUCASSIN: Nicolette, never depart
            From the hundred of my heart,
      Swim the sea nor ford the flood
            From the province of my blood;
      Ford the flood nor swim the sea
            To the coast of a far country.

NICOLETTE: Aucassin, for your dear sake
            Doleful journey must I make,
      And a greeting and farewell
            In the self-same breath must tell.
      And forever the strong sea
            Grieve between my love and me.

AUCASSIN: Nicolette, you shall not go! It would be the death of me!
      And I can read your future clear. The first man of proper
      feeling who laid eyes on you would be helpless to do
      other than lay hands on you and take you to his bed. Ah!
      Were your head to lie on any pillow but mine, I'd be so
      cut up I couldn't wait to fetch a knife to kill myself and
      finish the job.

            Why, I'd have to batter my skull against the nearest

wall so that my brains swam here and there like a colony of tadpoles and my two eyes jumped out of my face like a pair of frogs.

NICOLETTE: But it is on account of love that I fly. I cannot believe that your love for me matches it.

AUCASSIN: Quite impossible that your affection should be as great. There never was woman who loved man more than a man may love a woman. A woman's love lies in her glance, the bud of her breast, and at her foot's tip-toe. But a man's love is a seam in the mine of the heart. It is a deep root that may never be plucked out. Therefore, Nicolette, I beg you – never escape me.

[WATCHMAN *with lantern approaches on town wall above.*]

WATCHMAN: Three of the morning,
    Rising the day;
Soldier and citizen,
    Sleep while you may.

NICOLETTE: [*to* AUCASSIN]   Take this lock of hair to hand.

AUCASSIN: It shall be a wedding-band.

NICOLETTE: And upon this hand of mine
Do I wear a lock of thine.

[*Tableau, seen by* WATCHMAN.]

WATCHMAN: [*peering down*]   Well now, there's a handsome sight and no mistake. Enough to melt a block of Carrara marble to butter. And don't imagine I don't know who they are – or the price that's on their dear dewy little heads. And me a poor man, too. The sight of a spare shilling these days is enough to turn virtue into villainy faster than a goose-fair conjuror. As for a couple of them shiny chinkers, I've a feeling my wife would be willing to let me sleep with her all the rest of the days of her unnatural. Days, mark you, for I'm a night watchman. So pray don't think I'm any-wheres but on the good old Mount of Temptation up here, as usual.

But betray a brace of young lovers! Who could bring himself to do such a thing? I'll tell you, my friends. You.

Me. Anybody. It all depends on circumstances. And apart from the simple immorality of the thing, the way most marriages go nowadays, we might be doing everybody concerned a damned good turn, and there's a thought.

No, my dears. Circumstances, that's what we have to look at. And, given the need to do so, a man with his wits about him may so deploy an argument that he'd find himself able to accept a campaign medal for the Massacre of the Innocents. Particularly, come to think of it, if one of the innocents was one of his own – and born which side of the blanket as makes no difference.

After all, orders are orders: and I'm not after converting these good-conduct stripes on my arm into a halo. But if a man may do a good deed without being found out, let him do it, says I. Live, and let love, that's my motto. In any case, it isn't my daughter this young sprig wants to tack on to.

Stilled is the battle,
　　Camp-fires burn low;
Sleep is the victor
　　Of friend and of foe.

Citizen, soldier,
　　Sleep while you can:
Who knows what tomorrow
　　Brings woman and man?

[*Music presages the arrival of the Town Guard.*]
What approaches now? Is a watchman to have no peace – not even in the small of the night?
[*More music.*]
The Town Guard! Lanthorns! Drawn swords beneath their cloaks! God of Human Abundance, but they threaten their own manhood more than he whom they seek. Or she! This pretty, fair maid here is in danger of rape in the cape. Or even worse. Death! She must be warned – but subtly, or I'll be for trial without benefit of jury on my own account.
[*Sings, stressing various words.*]

Now from the eastward
　　Advances the light,
As walks *the watch*
　　In the last of the night.

Leave, pretty maiden,
　　Your couch of pure stone;
Leave you your lover
　　To lie there alone.

Let your tomorrows
　　Bring fair loving weather,
That free of sorrows
　　You lie down together.

Watch! From the sky
　　Strike the *swords* of the sun;
Love, like the hour,
　　Its true course must *run*.

NICOLETTE: Good Watchman, for the courtesy of your warning may the souls of your father and mother ever lie in the blessed repose of Paradise.

WATCHMAN: By Holy St John the Baptizer and Preacher, but this fair pretty creature's a fair pretty speaker! It's as rare a combination as a dainty roe-deer that also sings and plays the lute. Or cream on breast of chicken, as you might say – my common senses are so alchemized into a quivering jelly.

I'll risk giving the lady a slice of advice – and there's few greater liberties the old may take with the young. Nor with a greater promise of disaster. But here goes. Maiden!

NICOLETTE: My name is Nicolette.

WATCHMAN: Mark my song well, then, Nicolette my bird. And as I fear even you cannot fly, you must run.

NICOLETTE: By which road, Watchman?

WATCHMAN: The hardest. And the one your pursuers – damn their dusty feet and bright peepers – will think you least likely to take.

NICOLETTE: And that?

WATCHMAN: Over the town wall at its highest, and into the dyke at its deepest. Thence through the bitter swamp of water-snakes, and across the streamless plain. The Town Guard will never follow you there. Much too unpleasant. And dangerous.

NICOLETTE: But danger is the soldier's lot.

WATCHMAN: As his secret trade is to keep comfortably alive. You may count on that.

NICOLETTE: And after I have crossed the plain?

WATCHMAN: You are a Christian?

NICOLETTE: As I love my life.

WATCHMAN: Then pray to God. He's bound to think of something. And he's got more time than we have at the moment. Meanwhile, I beseech you. Go!

NICOLETTE: Watchman, for your love and charity I thank you with my most –

WATCHMAN: Dear Saviour, but how many have lost their lives and freedom from an excess of good manners. Maiden – fly!

NICOLETTE: Aucassin, farewell!

AUCASSIN: God be now your guard.

        [NICOLETTE *goes.*]

WATCHMAN: Citizen, soldier,
            Sleep while you can:
        Who knows what tomorrow
            Brings woman and man?
        [*To invisible Town Guard*]
        Halt! Who goes there,
            Weapons bare?
        Friend or foe?
            Eagle or crow?
        Red, white or blue?
            As if you knew!
        False or true?

Or, like me and you,
Something between the two?
   Eh?
Say!
   Speak – it is day!

SCENE 7

[NICOLETTE, *standing at a high level.*]

NICOLETTE: All-seeing Father, here I stand at the rim of a steep and
deep moat. If I leap down into its mud, I shall baste and
break my neck. If I stay, I shall be roasted in the fire. So, if
I am to perish, better here and alone than on show in the
market-square.
   [*She crosses herself; slides into the dyke.*]
Ah, but this is a stinking bed in which to lie! A farmyard
midden is a cradle of perfumes by comparison. And my
feet and hands bruised, bitten by nettles, bleeding! But I
am so seized with fear that I feel no pain. One thing to
descend here. Quite another to rise up and out. Now see
– a sharpened stake hurled down on the enemy by the
town's defenders!
   [*She seizes it and begins to scrape and dig.*]

Step by step I cut a stair
   And pray sweet Jesus has my prayer:

One is odd and two is even –
   As Jacob climbed up into heaven.

Three is odd, and even, four –
   I climb from hell to heaven's door.

Six and five are even, odd –
   Seven I stand at the gates of God.

   [*She has reached another level.*]
Or at least, before a waving forest, thirty leagues square if
it's a hand's breadth; and no more than two bowshots off!
Shelter enough there for an innocent fugitive, surely.
And home, I'll be bound, to a bestiary of wild animals; a

whole slither of snakes. If I penetrate its fastness far, one
or the other is sure to do me a mischief.

Jesu, Christ, I pray you speak –
    Which the path that I should take:

Through the thorny woodland wide
    Where the wolf and bear reside,

And the boar and lion seen
    Watching from their caves of green;

Yet if fear should stay me here
    Men will burn me in their fire.

Which of dangers is the least:
    Savage man, or hungry beast?

So, I pray in beasts to find
    Mercy more than in mankind.

[*She enters the forest.*]
As the light unveils its eye,
Hid in thicket will I lie:
    Safe from dagger, safe from claw,
    Hands of men and lion's maw;
Here will rest me, here will sleep,
Where the pleasant waters leap –
    Till the birds' first song is sung,
    And the bell at Prime be rung.
      Take my small rest,
      As bird in nest.

[*She conceals herself.*]

SCENE 8

[JOHNNY, TOM *and* DICK, *with flock.*]

JOHNNY   Early in the morning,
AND TOM: Hard crew the cocks,
    Three jolly herdboys
      Came with their flocks.

One was Spying Johnny,
    One was Tom Peek,
And one was known
    As Dicky-no-Speak.

Johnny in the sun
    And Tom in the shade,
And all they could talk of
    Was fair pretty maids;
How they'd stayed and laid 'em
    Seven days a week –
But never a word
    Said Dicky-no-Speak.

They'd loved 'em old
    And they'd loved 'em young,
But never a word
    Said Dicky-no-Tongue;
O they'd loved 'em rough
    And they'd loved 'em sleek,
But never a word
    Said Dicky-no-Speak.

Said Johnny, said Tom,
    Were a maid here now,
Her harvest we'd reap
    And her field we'd plough;
We'd work her land,
    No pay we'd seek,
But never a word
    Said Dicky-no-Speak.

O we'd scatter and sow
    And we'd seek no pay
Though we laboured twenty-five
    Hours a day;
We'd grind the grain
    For an eight-day week,
But never a word
    Never a word
    Never a word
    Said Dicky-no-Speak.

[NICOLETTE *emerges, barefoot, from her hiding place. Sensation.*]

NICOLETTE: God keep you, lads.

[JOHNNY *and* TOM *open their mouths, but are incapable of speech.*]

And may God be your aid.

[JOHNNY *and* TOM *gaze at each other, then to* DICK *for help.*]

DICK: God keep you too, lady.

[*Throughout the following, the thunderstruck* JOHNNY *and* TOM *attempt replies, but fail.*]

NICOLETTE: Do you lads know Aucassin, son of Count Garin of Beaucaire?

DICK: Very well.

NICOLETTE: Then tell him there is a creature in this forest he should come and hunt. And that if he catches the creature, he would not sell a single part of it for a hundred pieces of gold. Nor five hundred, come to that. Nor any price you could mention.

DICK: Me tell him that? Not on your life. You're having us on! There's no creature in the whole of this forest – whether it's a stag or a boar, or even a lion – whose limbs are worth anything like that. Bad luck to anyone who tells – or believes – such a yarn. You must be a fay, or a witch, my girl. My advice to you is to get going. We don't want anything to do with the likes of you!

NICOLETTE: Ah, but you will tell him. Do you not love Aucassin?

DICK: Indeed we do.

NICOLETTE: Then give him my message. For the creature Aucassin must hunt is that which holds the only cure that will ever heal him of his hurt. See, here are five-and-twenty pence from my purse. Take them. And tell him he has only three days in which to track down this quarry. If he cannot do so in that time, he will bleed from his present wound for the rest of his life.

DICK: [*uncertain*]   Tell you what. We'll hold on to the pennies. If he comes this way, we'll give him your message. If he doesn't, that's that. We won't be looking for him.

NICOLETTE: As God wills. Farewell.

[*She goes.* JOHNNY *and* TOM *are still trying to get a word out.*]

SCENE 9

BALLAD SINGER: Onward journeyed Nicolette
　　Where wild ferns and grasses fret,
On a path that green boughs span,
　　Till, as feathers in a fan,
All before her tender tread,
　　Seven forest tracks were spread.

Here, she said, I'll build a bower
　　Where to try and test my lover,
And she gathered *fleur-de-lis*,
　　Leaf and branch of ilex-tree,
And she made a house of love
　　In the freshness of the grove;

And she vowed should he not take
　　Rest within for her sweet sake,
Nor his oath nor promise prove –
　　Never more to be his love,
Never more of life to share
　　With Aucassin of Beaucaire.

SCENE 10

[AUCASSIN *in minstrels' gallery of the castle at Beaucaire. Feast and dancing in progress below. Enter* GARIN.]

GARIN: My God! Still standing sad as a gravedigger on the Day of Resurrection! Brace up, man. Have I not had you taken out of the dungeon of despair? Brought you into the light?

AUCASSIN: You have unlocked the prison door. For that I thank you.

GARIN: You look at me as though I had been party to a murder.

AUCASSIN: Have you, father?

GARIN: A son may not speak so to his sire.

AUCASSIN: Even if it is the truth?

GARIN: Particularly if it is the truth. In this case, it is not.

AUCASSIN: Men say that she is altogether lost.

GARIN: They also say that she is disappeared of her own accord.

AUCASSIN: Which am I to believe?

GARIN: All or none, it's the same to me. In the hope of raising your spirits a little, I make a rich feast in your honour. Music. Dancing. And all you can do is stand in the gallery with a face that would crack a fiddle-string.

AUCASSIN: She whom I love is far away. How should I look?

GARIN: [*patience lost*]   You should look to your inheritance, my son, or things might again go ill between the pair of us.

              [GARIN *stamps off. Dancing. Enter* KNIGHT.]

KNIGHT: Lord Aucassin, I too have suffered the sickness you now endure. I should like to instruct you. But all advice is useless unless it is that which the stricken one wishes to hear.

AUCASSIN: Then I shall trust you to speak it.

KNIGHT: Go from this place. It is poison to your spirit. Ride through the forest, over the pure grass and by innocent flowers. Listen to the notes of the birds. Who knows? You may very well hear something that will lift your spirits.

AUCASSIN: May God reward you, but this is just what I should do.
              [*He touches the* KNIGHT *lightly on the shoulder and rushes off. The* KNIGHT *does not notice his departure.*]

KNIGHT: Attend to the speech of streams. Swallow the scented airs. Spell out the sentences of leaves. Observe the moss-ed silences of rock and of stone. For mortal man may never stand alone.
              [*He looks about, and finds that he does.*]

SCENE 11

[JOHNNY; TOM; DICK. *The first two now wildly extroverted;* DICK *very much more restrained.*]

JOHNNY, TOM
AND DICK:
God bless Aucassin the fair;
    And the maid with springing hair
Gave us cash and gave us coin,
    Bought we cake and bread and wine,
Knives of steel and sheaths of leather,
    Caps to wear against the weather,
Flute and fife to pipe and play
    For a shepherds' holiday;
So we sing, and so we say –
    Bless the maiden, bless the may!

[AUCASSIN *has appeared during the song.*]

AUCASSIN: God be with you, lads.

[*Same effect on them as* NICOLETTE.]

JOHNNY: [*attempts to answer*]   Agh!

TOM: [*likewise*]   Ugh!

[*Pantomime from* JOHNNY *and* TOM *during the following.*]

DICK: And with you, Sir.

AUCASSIN: Will you all sing again that song?

DICK: Not to you, Sir. Nothing but bad luck will come to them as do, Sir.

AUCASSIN: Don't you know who I am?

DICK: As well as we know our parts, Sir. In our songs, Sir. You are Aucassin, our young Lord, and son of our master Count Garin of Beaucaire. But we are his men, Sir, not yours.

AUCASSIN: Sing it for me, I pray you.

DICK: By the Five Wounds, Sir, but we're not obliged to sing it for you unless we feel like it.

JOHNNY: Ugh –

TOM: Agh –

DICK: And we don't.

TOM: Agh –

JOHNNY: Ugh –

DICK: Mark us. We mean what we say.

JOHNNY: Ugh –

TOM: Agh –

DICK: There's no man in the whole country, except Count
            Garin himself, as would dare drive my oxen or cows or
            sheep off his grass or out of his corn, if they should have
            strayed there. Not without risking the loss of an eye. Or
            maybe two. I'm a man of my word, know that. Likewise
            Johnny and Tom here.

TOM: Agh –

JOHNNY: Ugh –

DICK: So don't expect a song at your command. Unless it suits
            us.

AUCASSIN: Here are ten silver shillings to help you change your
            mind.

            [*Enthusiastic gestures from* JOHNNY *and* TOM.]

JOHNNY: Ugh –

TOM: Agh –

DICK: [*swiftly*]   Never a note will I sing, Sir, for I've sworn not
            to do so. But I'll take the money all the same. And I'll *say*
            the words, if that's all right.

AUCASSIN: Better a speech than silence.

            [AUCASSIN *sits. Pantomime:* JOHNNY *and* TOM *– as*
            NICOLETTE, *with boughs, branches etc. – burlesque the
            story while* DICK *tells it.*]

DICK: At first of morning, between Prime and Tierce,
            Beneath the fountain of a forest tree,
            A maiden rose out of her hiding place
            Like Aphrodite from a leafy sea.

So fair she spoke, and shone as if with light,
And light she trod as though she were a fay,
The darkest corners of the wood burned bright
As was the coin she gave to us for pay.

'Tell my true-love', she said, 'here he may find
As he rides hunting in the heat, the cold,
A quarry rarer than the hart or hind,
And of such price as never man has told.

'And say, if limb of that sweet beast were his,
He would not sell for crown of gold, I wis.
For the hale flesh of such a creature heals
The wound within his heart that hunter feels;

'But in three days the quarry he must take
Or never more love's meeting will they make.'
This, my good Lord, I speak and say you true,
And keep my bargain with the fay. And you.

[*Exeunt* JOHNNY, TOM, DICK.]

AUCASSIN: God of love, now fledge my feet
      As my game I search and seek;
Neither running hind nor boar
      Fear my arrow nor my spear –
Nicolette my quarry be,
      That of love has wounded me:
Nicolette my prey shall fall –
      Cure my heart of lover's ill.

May the god of human-kind
Set my steps my love to find,
As beneath the stirring skies
Now I search and seek my prize.
Man nor beast nor fiend nor fay
Hold me from my chosen way:
That, unfaltering, I win
Nicolette my love again:
And from such quest
Will neither rest
      Body nor breath
Beneath moon, sun –

Onwards, and on
Till love is won.
That conquers death,
That conquers death –
    This is my path.

[*He goes.*]

SCENE 12

BALLAD SINGER: He rode the long brake at the pace of a shatter-pate
    Bearing a message for country or king –
He rode the long brake at the pace of a shatter-pate

Every thorn-bush it thwarted him, caught at him,
    Every nettle it gave him a sting.

Never a bramble but scribbled its name on him,
    Never a sapling but battered him blue –
Nipped him and ripped him, damn nearly unshipped
    him,
    And skinned him of cloak and of shirt and of shoe.

Grabbed him and stabbed him in places unmentionable
    In society common or fine –
Licked him and pricked him – an innocent victim
    Of bough and of briar, of thorn and of spine.

A man could have trailed him and fisted and mailed
    him
    For red was his track on the green of the grass –
But foe could not fight him, nor scar it could spite him –
    For thoughts of a lover must lie with his lass:
        All else is loss,
        All else is dross.
    The thoughts of a lover must lie with his lass.

[AUCASSIN *has entered at the end of the chase; weary,
dispirited.*]

AUCASSIN: Fall, dark.
Light, die.
Sink, heart.
Swim, eye.

Hunger and thirst,
Body's clay;
Love is here
And far away;
And far away.

> [*He sleeps. Music.* MARTIN OXBOY *rises up behind*
> AUCASSIN: *an immensely powerful and ugly young giant*
> *with a huge cudgel.*]

OXBOY: My name is Martin Oxboy,
Ploughman,
Of this earth and woody parish.
I am a young man of quite exceptional ugliness:
The hairs of my head the colour and feel of burnt meat.
My eyes planted a hand's-breadth apart.
My nose flat as a stretch of sand just ironed by the tide.
My sniffers wide as a pair of sea-caves near the same.
My lips are two strips of undercooked beef.
My teeth, a boneyard of neglected yellow tombstones.
Observe, too, my fashionable dress.

> [*He whirls about and displays it: bull's-hide boots, gaiters*
> *bound to above the knee with rope, and a reversible cloak –*
> *one side even rougher than the other.*]

And this, my accoutrement.

> [*Raises the great club over his head.*]

What an equipage for a boy-chap
In search of a good place in society!
Not to mention a suitable mate.
God be blessed that I'm sprung from a good family.
My great-great-grandaddy lived in Genesis Street;
Went travelling after he'd a-accidentally
Killed his younger brother as was a cow-keeper
And very religious. Settin' fire to sacrifice
He was, at the time.
My old Auntie Jezzie, bit of a princess,
Painted her face up like a picture
On a church wall
Down at the east end.
Fell out of a window, she did, poor old soul –
Must have been givin' the sill a wipe over.

And there's my Uncle Jone:
Signed on in the barque *Gospel Marine*
As a sea-lawyer;
Jumped overboard in a typhoon
To lighten the load
And took a second passage in the guts of a crocodile
Or some such fish.
Well, now, what's to be expected of me –
With such ancestry?
Think yourselves lucky, mates.
You come purling off quite another
Set of palm trees.
Character, that's what it takes
To overcome my lot.
But I got plenty o' that.
Dainty as a daisy, I am, underneath this rummage
Of wool and skin.
    [*He looks about the forest.*]
By God, but nature's wonderful!
You got to work among it to know it.
See that pretty butterfly?
No it ain't. It's a moth;
Gettin' a mite dimmit, it is.
A moth. An' tremblin'.
Delicate as a baby's tongue.
Look at them tame and tender colours!
Landed on a leaf, it has.
[*Appreciatively*]   Ah!

> [*He gazes at it, drooling. Suddenly brings his club up and over his head and deals it a smashing blow.* AUCASSIN *awakens, alarmed.* OXBOY *is still gazing intently at what was the moth.*]

OXBOY: [*sadly*]   Poor little animal. Looked sickly, it did. [*Instantly cheerful.*] Eased it out of this world of sadness and sufferin', that's what. It's happy now.

AUCASSIN: [*apprehensively; retreats a little on all fours*]   Fair brother, God be with you.

> [OXBOY *turns and notices him for the first time. Advances*

on AUCASSIN *and stands over him: menacing, club raised. Pause.* OXBOY *bursts into sobs; drops his club.*]

OXBOY: You must be the ninny I heard sobbing and sighing earlier on. You was making a terrible hullabaloo.

AUCASSIN: My dear fellow, but so are you.

OXBOY: Quite upset me, it did. I've just remembered.

AUCASSIN: Why should you weep?

OXBOY: If I had your legs and looks, and as much bullion in the bunker, nothing in the world could squeeze a tear out of me, I can tell you.

AUCASSIN: You know who I am?

OXBOY: You're Aucassin, the Count's son. These here eyes won't make a maid swoon, unless it's out of fright. But I sees pretty smart with 'em. And sounds come plain and clear into this pair of wagglers like bees to flowers. Tell me what you were yowling about, and I'll tell you what I'm up to here.

AUCASSIN: This morning I came to hunt in the forest. I brought with me a swift, white hound: the finest in the world. But he is lost, and I am weeping for him.

OXBOY: Just listen to that! All those crystal tears you're wasting over a smelly cur. Why, there isn't a baron in the land wouldn't be glad to make you a present of ten or fifteen or even twenty such hounds if your father permitted it. I'm the one who should be watering my cheeks and a-sprinkling my chops.

AUCASSIN: Then you must have good reason, I am sure.

OXBOY: A rich farmer hired me to drive his plough and team of four oxen. But three days ago I had the bad luck to lose the best of the bunch – Roger. O but I've searched and sought for him these hundred hours – and I've had neither food nor drink nor a sliver of sleep since the wretch abandoned me.

           If I go back to town without him, I'll be stuck in prison – no doubt about that – for I've no money to make up the loss. Here stands a man whose face is his present fortune!

I've no more in the world than what you see me with now.

AUCASSIN: But have you no family?

OXBOY: When my dear mother bore me, all she had was one miserable mattress, and this they pulled from under her to pay the midwife. It's sharp and naked straw she's lain on ever since! The thought of that stabs me more than my own present trouble. It's not myself is my chief concern. Easy come, easy go, that's me. I'll pay for old Roger some day. But my old mam – that's a different matter. What's to happen to her? And here you are, blubbering over a dog! Misfortune to anyone who thinks well of you after this, say I, if them's your principles.

AUCASSIN: Bless your heart, but you are a good comforter. You've cheered me up properly. Now tell me, friend. What was that ox worth?

OXBOY: [*bursts into tears again*]   My master says twenty silver pieces, and he won't take a halfpenny less.

AUCASSIN: A miracle! Exactly the sum I have in my purse. Hold out your hand and take it.

OXBOY: Sir, I thank you. And may the good God allow you to find what you are searching for.

AUCASSIN: God allow that. Farewell, my benefactor.

[AUCASSIN *goes.* OXBOY *watches his departure open-mouthed. Gazes at coins; puts them in his pouch. As he is about to move off, he spots another moth on his club. He observes it for a moment: an air of menace. Then, quietly*]

OXBOY: Moth! Moth!
  Light as breath.
Here is life.
  Here is death.
  [*He removes it from the club; holds it in his hand.*]
Wing, moth! And higher!
  To moon and star;
Kinder these are
  Than human fire.
  [*He watches it flutter up and away.*]

SCENE 13

BALLAD SINGER: Aucassin rode by the bush and the spray
                      Till seven green paths before him lay,
                  And there in the stare of the moon was a bower
                      Builded of boughs and the lily-flower.
                  This cot, he said, by the sycamore tree
                      Was built by my love for love of me;
                  Here I will lodge and here I will lie
                      And light from my charger heavy and high.

SCENE 14

[AUCASSIN, *writing. He has fallen, dismounting, and dislo-
cated his shoulder. He lies before the bower prepared by*
NICOLETTE.]

AUCASSIN: Twenty-five thousand tempests that have blown my
             lucky star clean over the horizon! Thinking of my dear-
             est, I fall from my horse on the only rock in this ocean of
             herbs. A fine situation for a prospective lover, I must say.
             What did you do when you first lay with your sweet,
             Aucassin? I fastened my mount to a thorn, swam into bed
             on my back like a capsized turtle, and lay groaning for
             twelve hours, boys. Laugh that one off, for I can't.
                 [*He crawls into the bower.*]
             Ow! I'll recite some verses, to take my mind off matter.
             [*He looks up.*]   My God! Holes in the roof. Stars! I can
             see the stars! Very romantic, but grant us a drought of
             raindrops for one night, O Lord, and an exemption of
             dew.

                 [*Somehow, he settles down.*]
             Star that glitters late and soon
             In the shallows of the moon,
             Were my true-love at your side
             Where those golden waters glide,
             Livelier far would be her light
             Than the fires of Sirius bright.

All the ridges of the air
Would I scale to join her there –
    And small be the price to pay
    If, earth-drawn by human clay,
        Icarus unfledged, I fell
    From that mountain to this vale
        Presently here.

[*Enter* NICOLETTE.]

NICOLETTE: Dearest and fairest friend. Well met!

AUCASSIN: Fairest and dearest friend. Well met also!

[*They embrace.*]

AUCASSIN: See! My shoulder was sorely hurt, but now that love is at my side I feel neither wound nor pain.

[*He winces.* NICOLETTE *performs healing-charm dance-song.*]

NICOLETTE: God who loves lovers
    Guide my white hand –
Simples to gather and heal a wound.

Here is a blossom
    And here is a bine;
With grass and sedges
    Now entwine.

Here is a bloom
    And here is a bud,
Plucked with the fingers
    Of maidenhood.

Here is a shoot
    And here a stem
Bound with a lappet,
    And tied with a hem.

Let no man know
    What is spelled or said;
Cured you shall be
    While blood is red.

Never you saw
   Of this my charm,
Cured you shall be
   Of body's harm.

In the name of Jesus
   And all his guild,
And sad, poor Judas
   Who died in the field:
     In, salve;
     Out, pain.
The spell is sealed.
     Amen. Amen.
   [AUCASSIN *is healed.*]

NICOLETTE: Now, Aucassin my dearest love. Let us decide what is best done next. If your father commands that this forest be searched tomorrow, and I am taken – whatever befalls you, death will most certainly be mine.

AUCASSIN: But must strike me first! Come! You shall see that against this day, I have trained my horse to fly faster than the wings of Azrael. Away!

   [*They go.*]

SCENE 15

BALLAD SINGER: By marsh and meadow
   And hill and moor
They rode till they came
   To the sounding shore.

And together they walked
   Those travellers three
On a beach of sand
   By the sliding sea.

And as they stood
   Between water and land
A ship there lay
   By the pouring strand.

   [AUCASSIN *and* NICOLETTE *hail the ship.*]

AUCASSIN AND NICOLETTE:	Where do you sail – Is it near or far?
SAILORS:	To the bay of Jerusalem. The coast of Navarre.
AUCASSIN AND NICOLETTE:	Where do you steer On the springing foam?
SAILORS:	To the islands of Antioch. The port of Rome.
AUCASSIN AND NICOLETTE:	Where on the jumping Main do you go?
SAILORS:	To Sinai city And Jericho.

AUCASSIN AND
NICOLETTE:
	Will you take us aboard
	    We travellers three
	Who wait by the side
	    Of the stalking sea?

SAILORS:	Come to the world
	    Of the white and the blue –
	And we'll show you such sights
	    As you never knew,

	In the world that the breathing
	    Waters span:
	The wonders of God,
	    And of beast and man.

BALLAD SINGER: They sailed in the still
    And they sailed in the storm;
They sailed in the cold
    And they sailed in the warm.

They sailed in the wet
    And they sailed in the dry,
Till the sea made a waterquake
    Mountains high.

But harbour they reached
    At World's End Bay,
And they dropped the hook,
    And they knelt to pray;

And the man and the maid
    And the milk-white mare
They stepped them down
    On the shining shore.

AUCASSIN: [*speaks*]   What is this land?

BALLAD SINGER: [*speaks*]   The young man said.

AUCASSIN: [*speaks*]   And whose is that barbican
    Stands o'erhead?

AUCASSIN AND   [*speak*]   Is it Greek you speak
NICOLETTE: Or the tongues of Spain?
Tell of your fortune?
    And tell of its fame:
Be it voice of a Gaul,
Or a barbarous bawl
From beyond the Wall,
Or best of all –
    In language plain.

[PEOPLE OF TORELORE *appear and all sing.*]

ALL: Never, ever, ever in the earth's long story
Was there such a kingdom as Torelore:
Where the icebergs burn,
And the hot-springs freeze,
And there's fire-bugs flying
In the snowball trees.

It's a fact
One can't deny
That every single roof is made of sky,
  And their oceans have no seas in,
  And their bumbles have no bees in,
  But their deserts all have trees in;
      And it's plain
      As any staff
That if they want to cry, the people laugh:
  It's a world so Topsy-Turve-ish
  That it makes a dervish nervous,
  For the straightest streets are swerve-ish
  And the squares are rather curve-ish;
      It's a both-
      -Er to discover
That your father might turn out to be your mother:
      And who can say
      For certain sure, he
Wouldn't lose what wits he had in Torelore?
So before we welcome strangers to our shore, we
      Declare a state
      That's hard to find
On maps and charts and items of that kind:
      And that we rate
      It a State of Mind
– A place from which most citizens might shrink –
      Though it's rather more familiar
      Than you'd think:
      Is Torelore!

CURTAIN

ACT THREE

SCENE 1

[KING OF TORELORE *lies on a truckle-bed: feet on pillow, head hanging over the end.*]

BALLAD SINGER: Through the land of Torelore
    Marched dread war with iron tread,
And the Queen, in armour suited,
    To the field of battle sped –
    All her warrior peoples led.

While the King, in close confinement,
    Feet where should have lain his head,
Family ways a-wandering, pondering,
    Sheets adrift and blankets fled,
    In child-labour lay abed.

TORELORE: Midhusband! Ow! Midhusband! To me!

[*Enter* AUCASSIN, *sword at the ready.*]

AUCASSIN: Midhusband? What is this midhusband?

TORELORE: Did you never hear of a mid*wife*?

AUCASSIN: I am Aucassin, son of Count Garin of Beaucaire, of as much education as any first-born young Lord in France. But I never yet saw a man in child-birth.

TORELORE: Be patient. You shall. Ow!

AUCASSIN: It's a mercy I left Nicolette below in the castle yard with my good charger. Such an awful sight as this might well incline a virgin maid from the lists of love for ever. And God alone knows what it might do to a horse.

TORELORE: The pain! There it is again!

AUCASSIN: At such moments a man must need the support of a wife.

TORELORE: She is away at the front.

AUCASSIN: Of what?

TORELORE: Of battle. Taking my place – temporarily, of course – as King and General. Leading the troops.

AUCASSIN: Is there war?

TORELORE: Great war. Ow! Why is the timing of child-birth always so extraordinarily inconvenient?

AUCASSIN: [*points*]   But *is* that the promise of a child, my Lord? It seems to me a cushion.

TORELORE: It may *seem* a cushion to you, young Beaucaire. To me – and to every father in my realm – it is an infant as yet unborn. Ow! Lie gently, my love.

AUCASSIN: [*wondering*]   Highness, flesh or silk, feathers or blood – that's as may be. But how may the bearing of such a load harm or hurt you?

TORELORE: Cruelly. Is not human creation by man and woman a mutual joy? And should not the labours of birth also be shared? We in Torelore consider the natural order to be somewhat unnatural in this respect, and seek to restore the balance. So – after a wife rises from her child-bed, her husband occupies it. For thirty days.

AUCASSIN: Forgive me, but I see no virtue in such a charade. Nor pain.

TORELORE: On the contrary, the pain that first has its source in the mind burns both body *and* spirit the more fiercely. This you shall know in good time.

AUCASSIN: Heaven forbid.

TORELORE: You will speak differently when your child is born and hangs at your breast.

AUCASSIN: No doubt.

TORELORE: Quite apart from the fact that there is no remedy.

AUCASSIN: But there is.

TORELORE: Really?

AUCASSIN: Really. Here. At hand. Merely rise. Exalt yourself, Highness.

[TORELORE *rises.*]

TORELORE: It's cold and dangerous up here. In my present state, my ballast has shifted somewhat, remember. I wish you'd get on with it.

AUCASSIN: You'll feel the benefit in no time, Majesty. Now! On!

[AUCASSIN *gives* TORELORE *a fearful drubbing with the flat of his sword, pursuing him about the room.*]

TORELORE: Madman! What are you doing to me? And in my own home, too.

AUCASSIN: [*furiously*]   Good-for-nothing son of a bad mother! Heaven help me, but I'll take the edge and point of my sword to you unless you promise me that no man will ever lie in child-bed in your kingdom again!

TORELORE: You would not kill me?

AUCASSIN: *Would I not!* Therefore pledge me your promise.

TORELORE: Pervert! You reverse the laws of nature!

AUCASSIN: If you say so, yes.

TORELORE: [*as though he is about to refuse*]   Never!

[AUCASSIN *makes a threatening gesture with sword.*]

TORELORE: [*hastily adds*]   . . . will I deny you this! I pledge! [*Ingratiatingly*]   Who knows but that your blade speaks with the sharpness of wisdom?

AUCASSIN: Sweet words, Highness, for lately in my own land I was the more often dubbed fool. [*He sheathes his sword.*] And now, a request. That my Nicolette remains here in your palace for rest and refreshment while you conduct me at once to where your wife the Queen is soldiering.

TORELORE: [*surveying the ruined bedroom*]   Two battlefields in one day! Mighty Alexander himself could desire no more! Besides, it shall be a paradise garden compared to this. So. Backward!

AUCASSIN: Highness, don't you mean 'Forward!'?

TORELORE: [*haughtily*]   Young man, I think you are forgetting where you are.

[*He marches out backwards,* AUCASSIN *following.*]

SCENE 2

[*The battlefield.* QUEEN OF TORELORE, *armed and with banner, surveying the land from vantage-point. Enter* AUCASSIN *and* KING OF TORELORE.]

QUEEN: Dearest heart! Husband! You should be a-bed!

TORELORE: 'Should' is as may be.

QUEEN: Not another mistercarriage?

TORELORE: I wish you wouldn't discuss these intimate matters before strangers, my dear. Well, hardly a stranger by now, what with one thing and another. Allow me to present the young Lord Aucassin, son of Beaucaire. [*In her ear*] Have a care, my dove. He's a bit . . . [*Hand gesture*] Not quite like us. You know. [*Whispers*] Abnormal. [*Hastily*] Can't help it, of course. It's an illness.

AUCASSIN: [*elaborate bow*]   I humbly greet you as subject and slave, Lady, and most meekly stand in the radiance of your beauty and the glory of your presence.

TORELORE: I say, steady on.

QUEEN: [*delighted*]   He sounds perfectly normal to me, my love.

TORELORE: But have no fear. You are quite safe.

QUEEN: Oh.

AUCASSIN: Ma'am, I see that you are soundly imbued with the first and greatest principle of victorious generalship.

QUEEN: Of course.

TORELORE: Certainly.

                [*Pause*]

TORELORE
AND QUEEN: [*together*]   What is that?

AUCASSIN: A sound supply of good food for the troops. This mighty
                pile of freshly-made cheeses, for instance. These eggs –
                bold and brown as the lusty hens that laid them! Field-
                mushrooms, each wide enough to ward off the squirt of a
                shower! And a whole beach of roasted crab-apples! Best
                field-kitchen I ever did see, Ma'am. It's obvious that
                you've studied the three great f's that make a soldier
                fight. The first two stand for food. So does the third.

QUEEN: Food! This is no food. It is ammunition.

AUCASSIN: [*staggered*]   Ammu – ?

TORELORE: [*firmly*]   – nition. Have you never been shot by a salvo
                of pears? Stabbed by a custard? Has your breast never
                been pierced with a pork arrow? Wounded with a fish-
                pie?

AUCASSIN: Not in battle.

QUEEN: Then you shall behold the horrors of vanquishment by
                victuals.

                [*She waves her standard, and with the* KING *recites the
                following. Accompanying physical movement is jerky as
                with mechanical figures of knights, etc. on – say – an ancient
                cathedral clock.*]

TORELORE   The cheeses are flying, the crab-apples plying
AND QUEEN: From hither to yonder and forward and back;
                 And puddings exploding – and now they're unloading
                     A petard of porridge done up in a sack.

                 Savaged by rye-bread and pie falls a warrior;
                     There lie his comrades all quartered with crumbs,
                 Ravaged and damaged by kale and cold cabbage,
                     Mastered by mushrooms and punished by plums.

Now the wild egg from the heaven's descending!
Down from the sky the dread sausages drop!
Things are nightmare-able! Almost unbearable!
Oh for the news of an armistice!
Stop!

AUCASSIN: Is the outcome of the battle unknown, Highness?

TORELORE: Not at all. Neither side has lost.

AUCASSIN: Then both are denied the consolations of victory?

TORELORE: Your logic is most extraordinary. If neither side has lost, both may be considered to have won. Do you follow me?

AUCASSIN: Not just at the moment.

TORELORE: Good. You will be as one of us in no time.

AUCASSIN: Those troops resting on their arms yonder. Are they or are they not your enemies?

TORELORE: My enemies.

AUCASSIN: And is their quarrel with you of long-time?

TORELORE: Looooooooooooooong-time.

AUCASSIN: I'd have you know, then, Highness, that I could put a stop to their little game here and now. Do you wish me to end the conflict, Sir? Once and for all?

TORELORE: Of course. Proceed at once.

[TORELORE *and* QUEEN *smile, embrace.* AUCASSIN, *to accompanying music, draws sword and lays about him with gusto. Horrified reaction from* TORELORE *and* QUEEN.]

TORELORE: Young man! Stop! There's no need to go as far as that. You will injure someone presently. I'd have you know that in these parts we never push a disagreement to the point where we actually kill one another.

QUEEN: Anyhow, further discussion of the subject is no longer necessary. The enemy forces have withdrawn.

AUCASSIN: Have you no interest in revenge? Or justice?

TORELORE: Justice, yes. Revenge – no: invariably a course of action incredibly boring and highly predictable. Let us speak rather of your beautiful companion Nicolette. You must introduce me.

QUEEN: Us.

TORELORE: Us.

AUCASSIN: Have you a daughter, Majesty?

TORELORE: A son.

AUCASSIN: Is he wed?

QUEEN: He is unwed.

AUCASSIN: Betrothed?

QUEEN: Nor that, either.

AUCASSIN: A man's man, perhaps?

TORELORE: Nor that, either.

AUCASSIN: May I inquire his age, Majesty?

QUEEN: One year and one day.

AUCASSIN: There is the sound of safety in that number.

TORELORE: Nor that, either.

SCENE 3

[NICOLETTE. *A room in the castle at Torelore.* AUCASSIN *enters during song.*]

NICOLETTE: Twelve of seasons now have flown
                Since to this rare land we came –
         And our love these summers three
                Green has grown as any tree.

         But the King upon his throne
                Would that I should wed his son –
         Prisons me by land and sea
                Till his child a man shall be.

And the King and all his sway
 Would my love were far away –
Would that Aucassin had passed
 From this country and this coast.
  Aucassin, my love, my dear,
  For our life and love I fear,
   In this place, drear.

SCENE 4

[*A room in the castle.* AUCASSIN *and* NICOLETTE. *Arab music. A great door crashes open. Enter* TARIK.]

TARIK: Surrender! I am a Saracen of considerable splendour! Useless to try and escape. This castle has fallen to a strong fleet manned by hardy and well-trained mariners, and of fighting qualities quite unmatched in the western world. Our peoples have invented sofas, dates, arithmetic, fountains, camels, total abstinence, and one hundred and fifty-three varieties of sex. Our extraordinary generosity of spirit and civilized behaviour towards captives and prisoners of war is renowned the world over.

I therefore advise you to lay down your arms and offer not the slightest resistance.

AUCASSIN: What happens if we choose death rather than dishonour?

TARIK: As you are hopelessly outnumbered, you are in no position to choose anything. That privilege is ours.

AUCASSIN: And your alternative to an immediate surrender?

[TARIK *whispers in* AUCASSIN'S *ear.*]

AUCASSIN: [*very rapidly*]   We surrender.

TARIK: Very sensible, if I may say so. Ladies this way, gentlemen that. We have two galleys reserved for prisoners. I trust you will not object to being bound hand and foot? And to a segregation of the sexes – we find such arrangements much less messy in the long run.

AUCASSIN: And the short?

TARIK: Especially the short. By the way, young fellow-me-lad,
          has anyone ever told you your tongue's too long? Take
          care that you keep it. I hope you get my meaning. Eh?

          [AUCASSIN *nods glumly. He and* NICOLETTE *are bundled
          out in opposite directions by two* PIRATES. TARIK *pro-
          duces a list.*]

TARIK: My memory's going. Now, what comes next? Pillage.
          Plunder. [*Turns list over.*] Rape. Such impossible de-
          mands on a warrior's energy! It's finished off more of
          our chaps than all the horrors of battle by land and water
          put together. And an infinitely dirtier death. Easy to see
          why we can't get the recruits these days. Anybody here
          want to change sides and sign on? No? Can't say I blame
          you. Yes? Think again, my friend. For the love of Heaven,
          think again.

          [*Yawns, stretches, exits.*]

SCENE 5

[AUCASSIN *and* NICOLETTE, *in separate boats, with* SAILORS.]

AUCASSIN: Row, ship, over the sea;
                 Fortune ill or fortune fair –
             Which of your faces
                 Awaits me there?

NICOLETTE: Ride, ship, the roof of the deep;
                 Sorrow or pain or hope or despair –
             Which of your gifts
                 Shall be mine to share?

AUCASSIN: [*spoken*]   In this craft a prisoner I,
             Under an iron cage of sky,
             Bound of hand and foot must lie
                 Till careless fate
                 Soon or late
             Tells if my stars shine cruel or kind,
             Of calm or storm, or sun or rain,
             Or if my love I meet again –
                 Who on another tide
                 Sails from my side.

NICOLETTE: [*spoken*]   Aucassin my dear heart's-core
             Journeys to a different shore;
             And the sweet mask that fate once wore
                 Like yesterday
                 Is cast away.
             Though here the sea lies still as snow,
             What storms may rise, what winds may blow
             About the sea-path he may go –
                 Ill-luck, sick weather
                 To part us for ever.

SAILORS: Fear not those blind coasts
                 Against which the ignorant seas
             Spring and start;
                 You bear your fortunes
             To those countries each
                 In your own heart.

AUCASSIN,   Ride, ship, the roof of the deep;
NICOLETTE   Sorrow or pain or hope or despair –
AND SAILORS: Which of your gifts
                     Shall be mine to share?

SCENE 6

BALLAD SINGER: Merrily sailed the summer ships
                     Over the summer sea,
                 When all at once a bag of wind
                     Burst loud as loud could be.
                         As loud as loud could be, my boys,
                         Over those ships all three.

                 The ocean it jumped all round about
                     As tall as a forest tree:
                 The sky it turned as black as tar
                     And the rain fell fast and free.
                         The rain fell fast and free, my boys,
                         Over those ships all three.

                 O the ship the wind blew to the west
                     It broke in pieces ten,
                 And the hungry water it swallowed down
                     Many a Sarsen man –
                         But never young Aucassin, my boys,
                         Never young Aucassin . . .

SCENE 7

[*The sea-shore; a gale rising.* JOHNNY, TOM *and* DICK *kneeling, arms raised. During the song,* AUCASSIN *is cast ashore and lies face-down.*]

JOHNNY, TOM   Early in the morning
AND DICK: The ship comes ashore –
                Clothes for the naked,
                    Food for the poor;
                God in his mercy
                    Send us storm-weather
                That we may keep body
                    And soul together.

                    [*They begin beachcombing.*]
                Mast for a roof-beam,
                    Plank for a door;
                Wine for the stomach,
                    Salt for the store.
                Rope for a halter,
                    Stem for a spade;
                Iron for the ox-plough,
                    Steel for a blade.

                Ships' tar and timber,
                    A case and a keg;
                A bootful of sea-weed
                    For Billy-one-Leg.
                A light and a lanthorn,
                    A sack of gold grain;
                A candle of tallow,
                    A fathom of chain.

                    [*They kneel again.*]
                For all these blessings
                    That swim here below,
                We thank thee, Almighty,
                    Who makes the storm blow;
                And bless the brave sailors
                    Under the sea
                Who send life and living
                    To sinners like we.

JOHNNY: Hold hard, boys. Here's a human fellow-creature that's flotsam-ed ashore, though whether he has breath in his lungs or sung just one psalm too many of water-music I can't tell yet.

TOM: Is he a nobleman, Johnny? Has he rings on his fingers and a silk lining to his breeches? An' has he any cash in his money-box?

JOHNNY: You're a vulgar, common, un-Christian jackanapes as would raid him before you'd aid him. Stand back.

TOM: Damn it, but don't you play the shammy, gentle-lamby Sammy-aritan with me, for it's well known you've more pickers and pluckers than an octopus has suckers. No – you speak so because you saw the body first, and claim all he has is yours.

JOHNNY: Hold your noise while I listens to the tune he's whistling on his bellows. If he's just played the Dead March, we're in luck.

> [*He bends down to listen.* AUCASSIN *suddenly sits up.* TOM *and* JOHNNY *dash to opposite ends of the beach.*]

AUCASSIN: What am I doing here?

DICK: Retreating from the water-gates of death, master. Welcome back.

> [JOHNNY *and* TOM *recognize* AUCASSIN *and are attempting to point this out to* DICK.]

TOM: Agh!

JOHNNY: Ugh!

DICK: And you are right. It *is* Count Aucassin of Beaucaire, as has been missing these three years.

AUCASSIN: I am Aucassin, of three years' exile in the land of Torelore. But not *Count* Aucassin.

DICK: Alas, my Lord, both your father and mother now partake of the eternal feasts of heaven.

AUCASSIN: Then may God rest them and invest them with His love, and – in His own time – may I too greet them in Paradise.

DICK: Amen. Now come, my Lord. Let us bring you joyfully to your castle at Beaucaire, where your lieges may vow fealty to you, and you may hold your land justly and rule it in peace. Truly, so shall all your men acknowledge obligation of fidelity, and swear. Swear!

TOM: Agh!

JOHNNY: Ugh!

> [*With great dignity,* DICK *escorts* AUCASSIN *off, lending him whatever assistance he may need, and signalling* JOHNNY *and* TOM *to bring up the rear. They scramble about hastily, gathering up what bits of jetsam they can, and follow on.*]

SCENE 8

BALLAD SINGER: And the ship that blew to the sou'-sou'-ee
It sailed to a southern strand
Where the sky burned blue and the palm trees grew
And the streets were made of sand.
The streets were made of sand, my boys,
On each and every hand.

As Nicolette gazed on the town,
On wall and tower high,
Her sudden heart was filled with joy,
And a tear stood in her eye;
And late she sighed and early cried,
Nor knew the reason why;
Nor knew the reason why, my boys,
Nor knew the reason why.

SCENE 9

[NICOLETTE, *aboard ship;* SAILORS.]

NICOLETTE: Whose is the ship that I sail in?

SAILORS: The King of Carthage.
Carthage King.

NICOLETTE: Who are these sailors about me stand?

SAILORS: Sons of the King
                     Of Carthage land.

NICOLETTE: Why do they wear the silk and pearl?

SAILORS: Half are Princes
                     And half are Earls.

NICOLETTE: Why do they make much joy of me?

SAILORS: They once had a sister –
                     Stolen was she.

NICOLETTE: Was she a mother or was she a maid?

SAILORS: Stolen she was
                     As a little babe.

[*The* SAILORS *now question* NICOLETTE.]

SAILORS: Where were you born and where were you bred?

NICOLETTE: Those who could tell me
                     Are long since dead.

SAILORS: Lady, your speech is gentle-true.

NICOLETTE: Father nor mother
                     I never knew.

SAILORS: Where was your living and where was your land?

NICOLETTE: Taken I was
                     On a far sea-strand.

SAILORS: What of that land do you cherish and call?

NICOLETTE: A tower of silver,
                     A snow-white wall.

SAILORS: A silver tower, a wall of snow?

NICOLETTE: Such as I see
                     Before me now!

SAILORS: To Carthage city we now are come.

NICOLETTE: Then Carthage city
                     It is my home.

SAILORS: Our father the King of Carthage be.

NICOLETTE: Then he his daughter
Soon shall see.

SAILORS: And your tender brothers true.

NICOLETTE: And I am sister
Of all this crew.

NICOLETTE AND Then let us say and let us sing –
SAILORS: That lost is found,
And joy is King;

Now land and sea divide us never:
And joy be King –
And live for ever!

SCENE 10

[*Carthage.* KING OF CARTHAGE; NICOLETTE.]

CARTHAGE: Stand not in awe of me. Simply tell me whom you may
be.

NICOLETTE: Sir, I am daughter to the King of Carthage.

CARTHAGE: That mighty King?

NICOLETTE: No less. As a little child I was stolen away from my home,
full fifteen years gone, and long years have dwelt in
France Kingdom, baptized and brought up as a Christian
maid. But when, today, the sea-galley drew under the
glittering walls of Carthage and I saw that city's white
temples and gleaming towers under a sky more blue,
more bright than any salt-water sea; when I saw its
thirsting countrysides, its proud castles, heard the music
of its fountains – I knew that this land was mine and that
home I was come. Alas, that now I am a stranger here.

CARTHAGE: All that you have said was done,
All that you have told is true –
Save one.
Here you shall be stranger none:
Nicolette, my child, my own –

King and father now have won;
And to his throne
Are you now a Princess come –

    And ere sun departs the day
    Let all people honours pay,
    Honours leal and homage bring
To the daughter of a King!

    [*Trumpets, etc.*]

SCENE 11

[MARINER; NICOLETTE.]

MARINER: The maid that was taken
    And now was found
To a Paynim King
    They would have bound.

Given in gold
    And marriage fee –
But Queen of Paynim
    She would not be.

She cared not for gold
    Nor Paynim dross –
But only for love
    That she had lost.

'I do not know,'
    The maiden said,
'If my love be living,
    My love be dead.

'But till my dance
    On earth is done,
I'll love no other
    By moon or sun.'

She took her a viol,
    She took her a string,
And to the sea-shore
    Herself did bring.

She stained with herb
　　Her face and hair,
And jacket and shirt and hose
　　Did wear.

NICOLETTE:　Tell me, mariner,
　　　　As you draw
　　Your anchor deep
　　　　From the ocean's maw,

　　Where do you journey
　　　　And where do you ride,
　　And a good ship's-boy
　　　　Do you need at your side?

MARINER:　Is thieving and murdering
　　　　Your employ?
　　Is this why you'd be
　　　　A salt-sea boy?

NICOLETTE:　A love I have lost
　　　　And would regain
　　Is why I would wander
　　　　The ocean plain.

　　And when to my love
　　　　My song I sing
　　It shall bind us strong
　　　　As a wedding ring.

MARINER:　Young man, cast off
　　　　The strong ship's cord,
　　And set your foot
　　　　On my fine ship-board.

　　On my fine ship-board
　　　　Shall you sing and dance
　　West and away
　　　　To far Provence;
　　West and away
　　　　To far Provence.

SCENE 12
[AUCASSIN, *dejected, in the castle at Beaucaire.* BARON *and
others present.*]

BARON: Aucassin, from sadness turn
            Now that summer sun is come;
            Over turret, under tower,
            Pipes the bird and spreads the flower
            As the scented air and bright
            Lifts the darkened heart to light.

AUCASSIN: All the colours of the day,
            Tunes the songbirds sing and play,
            Fill me all with dolour yet,
            For I have not Nicolette.
            Never on earth, in seas, nor skies,
            Dwells the heart content, while I
            Know not if she lives or dies.

BARON: As the heart of Saul was glad
            At the song that David made,
            Listen now to minstrel clear
            On the morning tide is here.
            He has sung in countries ten
            Of the love of maid and man;
            Learned is he of love's employ
            Though is but a beardless boy;
            And such history will share
            – Sweet as water, true as air –
            As was never heard nor told,
            Bought with silver or with gold,
                It is so rare.

            [NICOLETTE *enters, still disguised as a minstrel.*]

NICOLETTE: Listen now lordlings and ladies,
                Whether high or low are set,
            Of the love of Lord Aucassin
                For the faithful Nicolette.

            Such was love of man for maiden
                Kinsfolk would that she were dead,
            Prisoned her in tallest tower,
                Till to wild wood was she fled.

Aucassin his true-love followed –
Sailed they both upon the tide
And through shaking storm and tempest
Came to Torelore side.

Then to Torelore kingdom
Came the Paynim, wild and free,
And to Carthage bore the maiden –
But her lover – what of he?

Nothing of his fate or fortune
Knew the maiden of her lover;
But in famous Carthage city
Did her parentage discover.

In the mighty King of Carthage
King and father she has found
Who would wed her, who would bed her,
To a Lord on Paynim ground.

But to Paynim she will never
Give her love nor give her hand;
Vows that no man will she ever
Wed but gentle Aucassin.

AUCASSIN: Neither should he but Nicolette! But can you tell me any more of the maid of whom you sang?

NICOLETTE: Sire, I know her to be the truest of companions, as well as one of the wisest and most modest ever born. Her father is the King of Carthage, and it was to his land that she was taken when Aucassin also was made prisoner and borne from her side. On her arrival in Carthage, she was soon recognized as the King's daughter, and royally welcomed. Her father then desired to wed her to one of the greatest Arab Kings of Spain, but she declared she would prefer to be hanged or burned, no matter how great a monarch he might be.

AUCASSIN: Ah, my good friend. If you would only return to Carthage and invite her to come and speak with me, I would press on you more riches than you would dare to ask of me or receive. I tell you: for love of Nicolette, of whom you sing, I will take none other as wife. For me, it shall be Nicolette or no wife at all.

NICOLETTE: Sire, if that be your promise, then for both your sakes I will seek her out and bring her here, for I am fond of her too, and would wish nothing more than to see her happy.

AUCASSIN: That is my pledge. Forgive you these bright tears of joy that moisten my cheeks. My Lord Baron, I pray you pay this fellow twenty pounds, for it's a ballad of nights and days he's about to travel and tell.

BARON: [*produces purse*]   God, but that's a pretty price to pay for a song.

AUCASSIN: No price at all, as I remember, for such words, nor such music. Nor for such a singer, neither. You shall hear. And see.

BARON: [*pays money reluctantly*]   For all that, I most earnestly hope, Lord Count.

NICOLETTE: Trouble yourself no further on that score, sir. The song *shall* be sung. [*To* AUCASSIN] And keep your eyes clear of such heavy rain, master. In no time shall you see Nicolette.

AUCASSIN: Now that half a second of waiting is an eternity, what is no time? Six days? Seven?

NICOLETTE: Make it eight, my Lord. My song has a chorus, and I would never sing it to you now but whole.

SCENE 13

BALLAD SINGER
OR VISCOUNTESS:

A lady sat in Beaucaire city
    On a day,
Boy there came who at the gate-bell
    Did ring and play.
Dressed he was as merry minstrel,
    Viol in hand;
Dark his face, and was his habit
    Of a strange land.
'I will tell you of your fortune,'
    He did say.

'And of him who was your husband
　　Yesterday.
Once you took as child and daughter,
　　Saracen maid;
Was for love of a young Lordling
　　In prison laid.
Long time has that maiden fled you
　　To lands far –
Never thought you to behold her
　　Again near.
But a daughter's joy and duty
　　She bears you yet –
And would once more stand before you:
　　Nicolette!

'Pluck the yellow herb of brightness,'
　　The young man said.
'Anoint my breast, anoint my body,
　　And my head.
Bring the robe, and bring rose-water,
　　A silver comb.
You shall see again your daughter
　　Is come home.
In your chamber let a gown
　　Of silk be laid:
And there then shall stand before you,
　　Not man, but maid.'

All was done as had been spoken
　　And was sung;
Stood before the Viscount's lady
　　Maid that was man.
'To Lord Christ give praise, thanksgiving,'
　　The old woman said,
'That a daughter lost comes living
　　As from the dead.
May in heaven my husband dear
　　Rejoice amain
That the child of our affections
　　Returns again;

Rests now from the heart's long journey
   Seven days and one;
Then Aucassin, to his true-love,
   Shall surely come.'

SCENE 14

[AUCASSIN *seated, dejected. Enter* VISCOUNTESS.]

VISCOUNTESS: Lord Aucassin, weep no more. Come with me, and I will show you that which you love over everything in the whole world: Nicolette, your truest love, who has returned from far away to find you.

> [VISCOUNTESS *brings* AUCASSIN *to* NICOLETTE. *The following is performed by the whole company rather like the last scene in a pantomime.*]

ALL: When Lord Aucassin did hear
That his Nicolette was near,
Light his heart and swift his tread
To the chamber where she stood.
Straight into his arms she flew
As a bird to forest bough.

In his arms he held her fast,
Drew her to his breast at last;
Tenderly did kiss and play
Till the morning shine of day –
When to church his love he bore,
Made her Lady of Beaucaire.

Winter snow and summer breeze,
Autumn, spring – in joyful ease,
Never a tear, never regret,
Lived Aucassin and Nicolette:
Lived and loved, as they do yet.

For the tale that we have told
Is as new as it is old;
It is far and it is near,

Never was, yet it is here.
It is fable, it is true,
It is me, and it is you;
Here now ended, yet it starts
Ever in the human heart.

SPOKEN BY
ONE PLAYER: [*last line only*]   And is the story of our play.

CURTAIN

MUSIC FOR THE SONGS

NOTES ON THE MUSIC

The following pages contain a selection of sixteen songs extracted from the score of *The Ballad of Aucassin and Nicolette.* Their inclusion is intended to give readers some indication of the musical flavour of the work and also to whet the appetite of groups thinking of performance. It should be noted, however, that the music is represented in a somewhat simplified form (vocal line and chord symbols) – the work contains many inner and counter melodies which are of importance to the music as a whole. Although a full version of the work would not be poss-ible from what is given here, the performance of individual songs or groups of songs (perhaps as extracts) would be quite feasible. Intending pianists, guitarists or other chord instru-ment players are invited freely to decorate and embellish the basic chords (and, if necessary, simplify the more obscure ones) – always keeping to the spirit of the music.

The music was originally scored for a small ensemble con-sisting of oboe (doubling cor anglais), bassoon, violin and cello along with piano – the pianist directing the performance from the keyboard. Although a larger combination has since been used for the radio production, I feel that the original ensemble is the most practical for future performances. Of course a basic production could be given just using piano.

The songs vary in technical difficulty but do not necessarily need highly trained voices in order to render a pleasing perfor-mance. It is worth bearing in mind that the first company contained only one trained singer – the others were actors with good voices. Any dramatic group with upwards of six actors, some with reasonable voices, should not have excessive difficulty in achieving a creditable production.

STEPHEN McNEFF

♩ =72   NICOLETTE

D♭maj7/F   **D♭maj7/E♭**   **D7**   **C♯min7**

p espr.

Would that I could fly as free As the bird up - on the tree.

D♭maj7/F   **D♭maj7/E♭**   **Amin9**   **A♭maj7**

p cresc.   *f dim.*   *p*

In a pain - ted cage of clay I am locked for love a - way.

OLD WOMAN

p **E♭sus**   **C sus**

Turn the wheel — and foot the tread; Spin me strong a
Turn the wheel — and foot the tread; Spin a heart to

NICOLETTE *p* **D♭maj7/F**   **D♭maj7/E♭**

lo - vers' thread. Yet as strong as is the sea
rule a head

Dmin   **C♯min7**   **D♭maj7/F**   **D♭maj7/E♭**

p cresc.

Do I know my love loves me. Son of Ma - ry, hear me say

f **Amin9**   **A♭maj7**   **A♭min/E♭**

dim.   *dim.*   *p*

From this cell I must a - way With least de - lay.

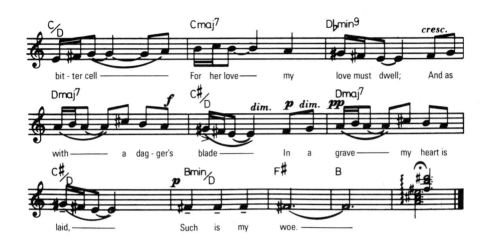

bit - ter cell ——————— For her love—— my love must dwell; And as
with ——— a dag - ger's blade ——— In a grave—— my heart is
laid, ——— Such is my woe. ———

ne-ver a word, it seemed, he heard U - pon their bloo-dy breath Un - til they sought his

life to thwart – Spoke of his death.

The Palmer's Song

pal-mer caught sight Of a limb so bright That a mir-a-cle then be-fell, my boys A mir-a-cle then be-fell. The

pal-mer a-rose as his blood it un-froze And his sick-ness it va-nished like snow, And for e-ver and aye for ten years and a day A

pil-grim-ming he did go, my boys, A pil-grim-ming go-go-go. And he swore that for him the sight of the limb Of a

li-ly-white la-dy fair Was bet-ter by half than a doc-tor's draught, And me-di-cine free as air Far —

bet-ter than a doc-tor's care, And good for both bo-dy and soul, my boys, For bo-dy and so-so-soul. And

good for both bo-dy and soul, my boys, For bo-dy and so-so-soul.

(continued overleaf)

♩=92 BALLAD SINGER

On-ward jour-neyed Ni - co - lette Where wild ferns and
Here, she said, I'll build a bower Where to try and
And she vowed should he not take Rest wi - thin for

gras-ses fret, On a path that green boughs span – Till, as fea - thers
test my lover, And she ga - thered *fleur - de - lis,* Leaf and branch of
her sweet sake, Nor his oath nor pro - mise prove – Ne - ver more to

in a fan, All be - fore her ten - der tread Se - ven fo - rest
i - lex - tree, And she made a house of love In the fresh-ness
be his love, Ne - ver more of life to share With Au - cas - sin

tracks were spread.
of the grove;
of Beau - caire.

Martin Oxboy's Song

♩=69

Moth!

Moth! Light as breath. —— Here is life.

Here is death. Wing, moth! And high - er! To moon and star;

—— Kin - der these are Than hu - man fire.

Top-sy - Turve - ish That it makes a der - vish ner - vous,

For the straigh-test streets are swerve-ish And the squares are ra - ther curve - ish;

It's a both-er To dis - co - ver That your

fa-ther might turn out to be your mo-ther: And who can say For cer - tain sure, he

Would-n't lose what wits he had in Tor - e - lor-e? So be - fore we wel-come stran-gers to our shore, we

De - clare a state That's hard to find On

maps and charts and i - tems of that kind;

And that we rate It a State of Mind – A place from which most ci - ti-zens might shrink – Though it's

ra - ther more fa-mi - liar Than you'd think: Is Tor - e - lor - e!

NICOLETTE

Twelve of sea-sons now have flown   Since to this rare land we came –   And our love these sum-mers three

Green has grown as a - ny tree.   But the King u - pon his throne   Would that I should wed his son –

Pri-sons me by land and sea   Till his child a man shall be.   And the King and all his sway

Would my love were far a - way –   Would that Au - cas-sin had passed From this coun - try and this coast.

Au-cas-sin, my love, my dear,   For our life and love I fear,   In this place,   drear.

Lis-ten now lord-lings and la-dies,   Whe-ther high or low are set,   Of the love of Lord Au-cas-sin
Au-cas-sin his true-love fol-lowed – Sailed they both u-pon the tide   And thro' sha-king storm and tem-pest

For the faith-ful Ni-co-lette.   Such was love of man for mai-den   Kins-folk would that she were dead,
Came to Tor - e - lor - e side.   Then to Tor - e - lor - e king - dom   Came the Pay-nim, wild and free,

Pri-soned her in tal-lest to-wer,   Till to wild wood was she fled.   No-thing of his fate or for-tune
And to Car-thage bore the mai-den – But her lo - ver – what of he?

Knew the   mai - den   of   her   lo - ver;   But in   fa - mous   Car-thage ci - ty

Did her pa-ren-tage dis-co-ver.   In the migh-ty King of Car-thage! King and fa-ther she has found

Who would wed her, who would bed her, To   a Lord on Pay-nim ground.   But to Pay-nim she will ne - ver

Give her love nor give her hand;   Vows that no man will she e-ver   Wed but gen-tle Au-cas-sin.

♩=108

Accomp.

ALL

When   Lord Au - cas - sin   did hear
In   his arms   he   held   her fast,

That   his Ni - co - lette   was near,
Drew   her to   his   breast   at last;

Light   his heart and   swift   his tread
Ten - der - ly   did   kiss   and play

To   the cham - ber   where she stood.
Till   the mor - ning   shine   of day –

Straight in - to   his   arms   she flew
When   to church   his   love   he bore,

As   a bird   to   fo-rest   bough.
Made   her La - dy   of Beau - caire.

Win - ter snow   and   sum - mer breeze,

Au - tumn, spring – in   joy - ful ease,

Ne - ver a tear,   ne - ver re-gret,   Lived

Au - cas - sin   and   Ni - co - lette:

Lived and loved   as   they   do yet.

rit.

(continued overleaf)

For the tale —— that we have told Is as new —— as it is old;

It is far —— and it is near, Ne-ver was, —— yet it is here.

It is fa - - ble, it is true, It is me, —— and it is you;

Here now en - ded, yet it starts E - ver in —— the hu-man heart. [Spoken] And is the story of our play.